Structural Arithmetic III

Margaret Stern
Toni S. Gould

ADDITION

A Solve for *X*.

$X = 8 + 9$ $X = 4 + 9$ $X = 9 + 3$

$X = $ _____ $X = $ _____ $X = $ _____

$X = 45 + 10$ $X = 30 + 9$ $X = 10 + 7$

$X = $ _____ $X = $ _____ $X = $ _____

B

8	9	8	7	5	8	7	9
+ 3	+ 5	+ 7	+ 6	+ 6	+ 5	+ 4	+ 7

7	6	9	6	8	6	8	7
+ 5	+ 8	+ 0	+ 5	+ 4	+ 7	+ 6	+ 7

4	9	5	4	8	6	9	3
+ 7	+ 3	+ 7	+ 8	+ 8	+ 9	+ 2	+ 8

C

Ms. Black has **8** students in her third-grade class. Mr. Dodd has **9** students in his third-grade class. The two classes have music together. How many students are in the music class?

Hattie has **5** goldfish in her tank. Ed has **9** goldfish in his tank. How many goldfish do they have altogether?

_____ students are in the music class.

They have _____ goldfish altogether.

1

COLUMN ADDITION

A

Add the numbers.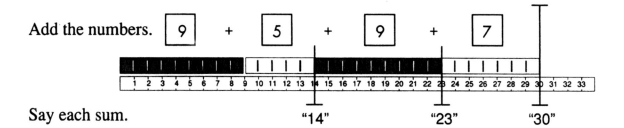

Say each sum.   "14"   "23"   "30"

B

9 + 5 = ____   3 + 7 = ____   6 + 6 = ____

19 + 5 = ____   13 + 7 = ____   16 + 6 = ____

29 + 5 = ____   23 + 7 = ____   26 + 6 = ____

4 + 9 = ____   4 + 6 = ____   8 + 8 = ____

14 + 9 = ____   14 + 6 = ____   18 + 8 = ____

24 + 9 = ____   24 + 6 = ____   28 + 8 = ____

C

9	6	7	8		3	6	8	8
5	3	9	9		9	4	8	9
9	9	6	7		9	7	4	7
+ 7	+ 2	+ 9	+ 6		+ 9	+ 7	+ 7	+ 6

5	8	6	6		8	9	9	4
9	8	9	6		2	5	8	5
4	9	5	9		6	9	3	8
+ 9	+ 5	+ 6	+ 7		+ 9	+ 4	+ 6	+ 9

2

A

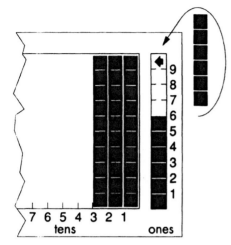 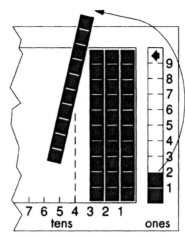 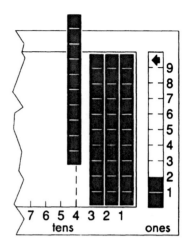

3 6	$\overset{1}{3}$ 6	3 6
+ 6	+ 6	+ 6
	——	——
	2	

Add the ones:
  6 + 6 = 12.
If there are more
  than 10 ones, you
  must regroup.

Exchange 10 ones
  for 1 ten.
Write **2** in the ones place.
Carry 1 ten to the tens place.
Write a small **1** above 3 tens.
Add the tens: 1 + 3 = 4.

Do the example.

B

56	88	47	69	89	75
+ 7	+ 9	+ 5	+ 5	+ 7	+ 8

14	36	27	74	63	57
+ 29	+ 49	+ 35	+ 17	+ 28	+ 37

3

A   9 + 6 = _____   5 + 7 = _____   5 + 6 = _____

19 + 6 = _____   15 + 7 = _____   15 + 6 = _____

29 + 6 = _____   25 + 7 = _____   25 + 6 = _____

7 + 9 = _____   8 + 4 = _____   6 + 7 = _____

17 + 9 = _____   18 + 4 = _____   16 + 7 = _____

27 + 9 = _____   28 + 4 = _____   26 + 7 = _____

8 + 9 = _____   7 + 5 = _____   7 + 8 = _____

18 + 9 = _____   17 + 5 = _____   17 + 8 = _____

28 + 9 = _____   27 + 5 = _____   27 + 8 = _____

B

36	13	22	38	25
43	24	32	17	46
+ 19	+ 45	+ 18	+ 32	+ 17

15	28	35	47	14
29	17	16	15	34
38	39	26	18	17
+ 15	+ 15	+ 18	+ 13	+ 25

A

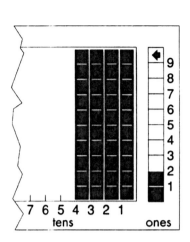

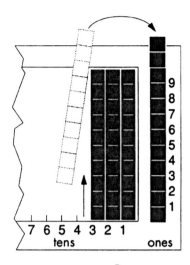

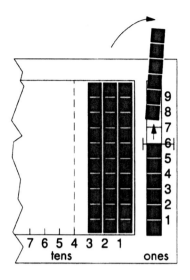

4 2	3 1 4̶ 2	4 2
− 6	− 6	− 6
	6	

Look at the ones.
You cannot take 6 ones
   away from 2 ones.
You must regroup.

Carry back 1 ten to the ones place.
Exchange 1 ten for 10 ones.
Write a small 1 next to the 2.
Cross out the 4.
Write a 3 above the 4.
Subtract.

Do the example.

B

38	55	64	96	84	72	75
− 9	− 8	− 8	− 9	− 7	− 3	− 7

83	61	47	42	32	93	23
− 6	− 3	− 8	− 8	− 7	− 8	− 7

5

REGROUPING IN SUBTRACTION

A

17	16	13	15	13	16	14
− 9	− 9	− 9	− 9	− 4	− 7	− 5

12	12	12	12	11	15	17
− 5	− 7	− 8	− 4	− 5	− 7	− 8

16	14	12	18	11	11	11
− 8	− 7	− 6	− 9	− 7	− 6	− 8

B

31	46	51	95	62	71	82
− 14	− 28	− 38	− 57	− 47	− 47	− 38

58	67	42	73	76	34	83
− 29	− 38	− 15	− 47	− 47	− 19	− 34

84	81	55	91	67	44	33
− 67	− 55	− 29	− 78	− 49	− 25	− 26

A   Add or subtract.

29	37	52	38	37	77
+ 66	+ 38	− 38	+ 58	− 19	+ 15

73	56	66	55	62	27
− 49	− 48	− 27	+ 37	− 27	+ 67

73	15	65	55	62	82
− 46	+ 44	+ 26	+ 25	− 13	− 54

B   Add.

12	23	15	16	38	37
25	16	47	21	23	34
+ 34	+ 35	+ 34	+ 38	+ 28	+ 28

C

18 children are in grade 1 at King School. 33 children are in grade 2, and 38 children are in grade 3. How many children go to King School?

Jonathan saw 45 horses and 34 monkeys at the circus. How many more horses were there than monkeys?

_____ children go to King School.

There were _____ more horses than monkeys.

7

ROMAN NUMERALS

A Write the numerals we use today.

I _____

II _____

III _____

IV _____
1 before 5

V _____

VI _____
5 + 1

VII _____
5 + 2

VIII _____
5 + 3

IX _____
1 before 10

X _____
5 + 5

B Write the numerals we use today.

XI _____   XIX _____   XXVI _____

XV _____   XVIII _____   XXX _____

XIII _____   XVII _____   XXIX _____

XII _____   XVI _____   XXVIII _____

XIV _____   XX _____   XXVII _____

C Write the sums in Roman numerals.

VII + V = __XII__   VIII + VII = _____   X + VI = _____

VIII + V = _____   XI + XXII = _____   V + V = _____

8

SEPTEMBER						
Sunday	Monday	Tuesday	Wednesday	Thursday	Friday	Saturday
		1	2	3	4	5
6	7	8	9	10	11	12
13	14	15	16	17	18	19
20	21	22	23	24	25	26
27	28	29	30			

Look at the calendar. Which day does the first of September fall on?

_____

Find all the Tuesdays. They are

September _____, _____, _____, _____,

and _____.

How many days does the month of

September have? _____

Write the date of the last day of September.

_____

Write the date of the first Saturday in September.

_____

Draw a line around the first three days of September.

Which day is the third of September?

_____

A week starts on Sunday and ends with Saturday. Shade in one of the weeks on this calendar with your pencil.

MONTHS OF THE YEAR

A

1 January

2 February

3 March

4 April

5 May

6 June

7 July

8 August

9 September

10 October

11 November

12 December

B   Write the number of each month. Check with the pictures above.

March	3	August	____	September	____
January	____	July	____	December	____
April	____	May	____	November	____
February	____	June	____	October	____

The month in which my birthday comes is

_____.

My birthday is in month number _____.

The date of my birthday is

_____.

Valentine's Day comes in

_____.

Halloween comes in

_____.

FINDING THE SUM	FINDING HOW MANY ARE LEFT

A

9 girls and 8 boys are coming to the birthday party. How many children are coming to the party?

Known		Unknown
first addend	second addend	sum
9	+ 8	= ?

_____ children are coming.

B

The children made a toy town with blocks. Jason used 2 blocks, and Jill used 15 blocks. How many blocks did they use to make the toy town?

The children used _____ blocks.

The first grade found 9 seed pods for science class. The second grade found 9 seed pods. How many seed pods did they have for science class that day?

They had _____ seed pods.

C

There are 25 children in the third-grade class. 5 children got sick and went home. How many children were left in school?

Known		Unknown
total	amount gone	remainder
25	− 5	=

_____ children were left in school.

D

There were 44 cabbages in Samantha's garden. She fed 10 of them to her rabbits. How many cabbages were left?

_____ cabbages were left.

The pet store had 40 goldfish. It sold 10 to the school for its pond. How many goldfish were left in the pet store?

There were _____ goldfish left.

11

A

Al needs 14 chairs for his club meeting. He has 9 chairs. How many more chairs does Al need?

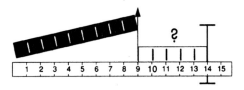

Known		Unknown
total wanted	the amount on hand	how many more are needed
14	− 9	=

Al needs _____ more chairs.

B

It is 13 miles from Terry's house to the fair. After 8 miles Terry stops to eat lunch. How many more miles does Terry need to drive to get to the fair?

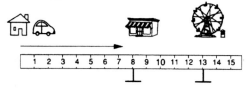

Known		Unknown
total trip	miles driven	miles to go
13	− 8	=

Terry needs to drive _____ more miles.

C

Kate needs $15 to buy a toy. She has $9 in her bank. How much more money does she need?

Kate needs $_____ more.

The bus must drive 50 miles to get to the beach. After it has gone 20 miles, it stops for gas. How many more miles must the bus go to reach the beach?

The bus must go _____ more miles.

The third graders need 18 plates for their class picnic. They have 9 plates. How many more plates do they need?

They need _____ more plates.

It will take Dad 12 hours to paint the car. If he stops after 4 hours, how many more hours must he work to finish the job?

Dad must work _____ more hours.

A

Sue is growing **18** tulips. **4** tulips are red and the rest are white. How many tulips are white?

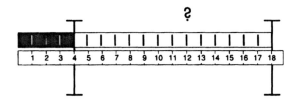

How to find the rest:
    Subtract the known part from the total.

Known		Unknown
total	one part	the rest

18	–	4	=	?

18	–	4	=	

Sue has _____ white tulips.

B

There are **40** children in our school play. **20** of them are boys. The rest are girls. How many girls are in the play?

There are _____ girls in the play.

The twins went to camp for **14** days. It was sunny on **9** days. It rained the rest of the days. How many days did it rain?

It rained _____ days.

Peggy has **18** thank-you letters to write. She wrote **11** of them before lunch. She will write the rest after lunch. How many letters will she write after lunch?

Peggy will write _____ letters after lunch.

On Friday our class of **24** children took a trip. Last week **20** children went on the trip. The rest were absent. How many children were absent?

_____ children were absent.

A

Manuel has 17 books. Laurie has only 8 books. How many more books does Manuel have than Laurie?

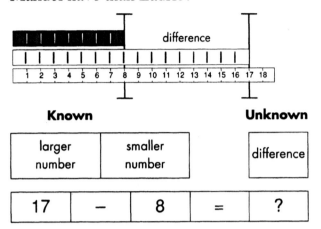

Known **Unknown**

larger number	smaller number		difference

17	–	8	=	?

How to find the difference:
   Subtract the smaller number from the larger number.

17	–	8	=	

Manuel has _____ more books than Laurie has.

B

To get home Alex must drive 90 miles. Nancy drives only 60 miles to get home. How many fewer miles will Nancy drive?

Nancy will drive _____ fewer miles than Alex.

The second grade put 40 paintings in the art show. The third grade put 50 paintings in the show. How many more paintings did the third grade put in the art show?

The third grade put in _____ more paintings.

There are 20 children on the baseball team. There are 30 children on the soccer team. How many fewer children are there on the baseball team?

There are _____ fewer children on the baseball team.

There are 17 birds in the pet store and only 9 kittens. How many more birds are there than kittens?

There are _____ more birds.

A

Solve the problems.

The door of Sam's penny bank opened. 18 pennies rolled out. He found only 12. How many were lost?

There are 14 apples in the fruit basket. 8 are red. The rest are yellow. How many apples are yellow?

_____ pennies were lost.

_____ apples are yellow.

The children had 7 paper cups at their lemonade stand. They found 13 more. How many paper cups did they have then?

The teacher wants to give each of her 15 children a note to take home. She has written 8 notes. How many more notes must she write?

They had _____ paper cups.

The teacher must write _____ more notes.

B

Write the Roman numerals.

1 _____   6 _____   11 _____   16 _____

2 _____   7 _____   12 _____   17 _____

3 _____   8 _____   13 _____   18 _____

4 _____   9 _____   14 _____   19 _____

5 _____   10 _____   15 _____   20 _____

C

Complete the sentences.

The first month of the year is

_____.

It is month number _____.

The last month of the year is

_____.

It is month number _____.

TEST

A

Solve the problems.

16 children were playing outside. Then 7 children went inside. How many children stayed outside?

_____ children stayed outside.

Grandpa runs a pet store. He has 17 empty cages. He put animals in 8 of the cages. How many more cages does Grandpa have to fill?

Grandpa has to fill _____ more cages.

There are 12 boys in the school band and only 8 girls. How many more boys are there than girls?

There are _____ more boys than girls.

Christina weighs 50 pounds. Her brother weighs 60 pounds. How many more pounds does her brother weigh?

Her brother weighs _____ pounds more than Christina.

B

Write the Roman numerals.

21 _____   24 _____   27 _____

22 _____   25 _____   28 _____

23 _____   26 _____   29 _____

C

Complete the sentences.

The sixth month of the year is

_____.

The date of my birthday is

_____.

The third month of the year is

_____.

Thanksgiving Day comes in

_____.

16

A

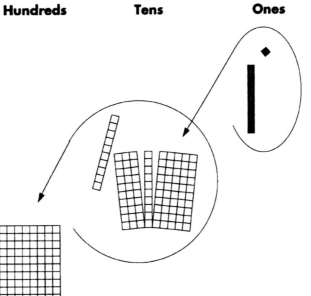

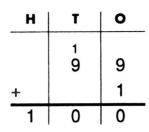

Exchange 10 ones
for 1 ten.

Then exchange 10 tens
for 1 hundred.

Hundreds	Tens	Ones
1	0	0

H	T	O
	1	
	9	9
+		1
1	0	0

B Write the numbers.

Hundreds	Tens	Ones	

 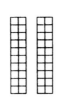

one hundred forty-three

___   ___   ___   ___ ___ ___

C

581	616	378	354	453	537
+ 409	+ 374	+ 414	+ 537	+ 228	+ 256

A

```
  2 7 2
+   3 0
```

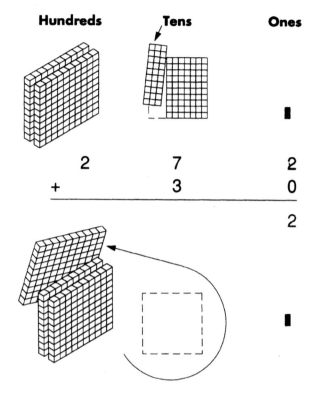

Hundreds   **Tens**   **Ones**

```
    2          7          2
  +            3          0
  _____
                          2
```

Add the ones: 2 + 0 = 2.
Write <u>2</u> in the ones place.
Add the tens: 7 + 3 = 10.
You must regroup.

```
  1
  2 7 2
+   3 0
_____
    0 2
```

Exchange 10 tens for 1 hundred.
Write <u>0</u> in the tens place.
Carry 1 hundred to the hundreds place.
Write a small <u>1</u> above 2 hundreds.
Add the hundreds: 2 + 1 = 3.

B

272	554	725	231	664
+ 30	+ 50	+ 81	+ 73	+ 45

472	363	243	534	777
+ 146	+ 265	+ 666	+ 384	+ 52

A

```
  4 2 7
+   7 3
```

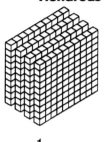

Hundreds   **Tens**   **Ones**

Add the ones: 7 + 3 = 10.
You must regroup.
Exchange 10 ones for 1 ten.
Write 0 in the ones place.
Carry 1 ten to the tens place.
Write a small 1 above 2 tens.

```
    1
  4 2 7
+   7 3
  ─────
      0
```

Add the tens: 2 + 1 + 7 = 10.
You must regroup.
Exchange 10 tens for 1 hundred.
Write 0 in the tens place.
Carry 1 hundred to the hundreds place.
Write a small 1 above 4 hundreds.
Add the hundreds: 4 + 1 = 5.

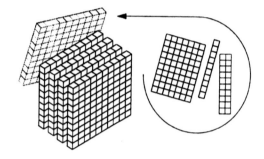

```
  1 1
  4 2 7
+   7 3
  ─────
    0 0
```

B

427	624	825	438	747
+ 73	+ 76	+ 75	+ 62	+ 53
482	573	646	769	287
+ 49	+ 89	+ 68	+ 58	+ 35

A

```
  4 2 5
-   3 0
```

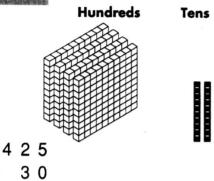

Hundreds   **Tens**   **Ones**

Subtract the ones: 5 – 0 = 5.
Write 5 in the ones place.
Look at the tens.
You cannot take 3 tens away from 2 tens.
You must regroup.

```
  4 2 5
-   3 0
      5
```

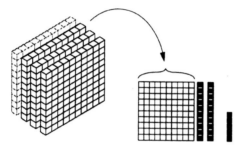

Carry back 1 hundred to the tens place.
Exchange 1 hundred for 10 tens.
Write a small 1 next to the 2.
Cross out the 4; write a 3 above the 4.
Subtract the tens: 12 – 3 = 9.
Write 9 in the tens place.
Subtract the hundreds: 3 – 0 = 3.
Write 3 in the hundreds place.

```
   3 1
   4 2 5
 -   3 0
       5
```

B

425	848	589	457	747
– 30	– 54	– 92	– 76	– 53

735	968	963	316	287
– 84	– 85	– 91	– 23	– 94

A

```
  4 3 5
- 1 6 7
```

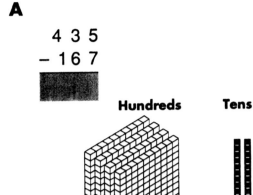

Hundreds   **Tens**   **Ones**

Look at the ones.
You cannot take 7 ones away from 5 ones.
You must regroup.
Carry back 1 ten to the ones place.
Exchange 1 ten for 10 ones.
Write a small 1 next to the 5.
Cross out the 3; write a 2 above the 3.
Subtract the ones: 15 – 7 = 8.
Write 8 in the ones place.

```
    2 1
  4 3 5
- 1 6 7
───────
      8
```

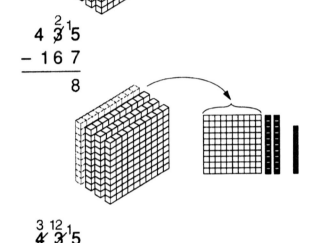

Look at the tens.
You cannot take 6 tens away from 2 tens.
You must regroup.
Carry back 1 hundred to the tens place.
Exchange 1 hundred for 10 tens.
Write a small 1 next to the 2.
Cross out the 4; write a 3 above the 4.
Subtract the tens: 12 – 6 = 6.
Write 6 in the tens place.
Subtract the hundreds: 3 – 1 = 2.
Write 2 in the hundreds place.

```
  3 12 1
  4 3 5
- 1 6 7
───────
      8
```

B

435	766	753	956	535
− 167	− 598	− 294	− 576	− 366
735	883	573	826	753
− 479	− 598	− 477	− 397	− 476

A

```
  3 0 4
-   5 5
```

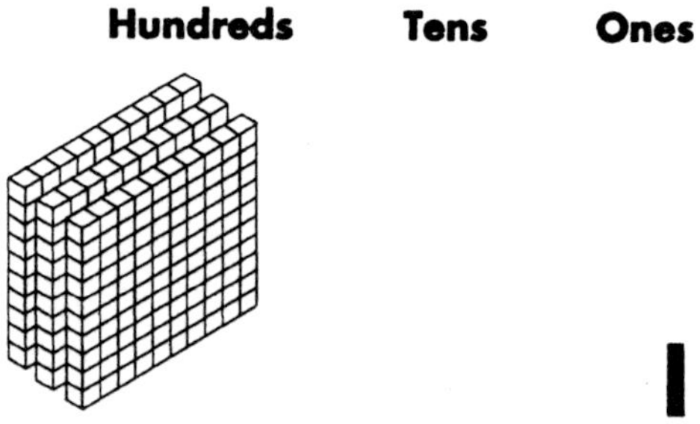

Look at the ones.
You cannot take 5 ones away from 4 ones.
You must regroup.
Look at the tens.
You cannot carry back 1 ten from 0 tens.
You must regroup again.
Look at the hundreds.

```
  3 0 4
-   5 5
```

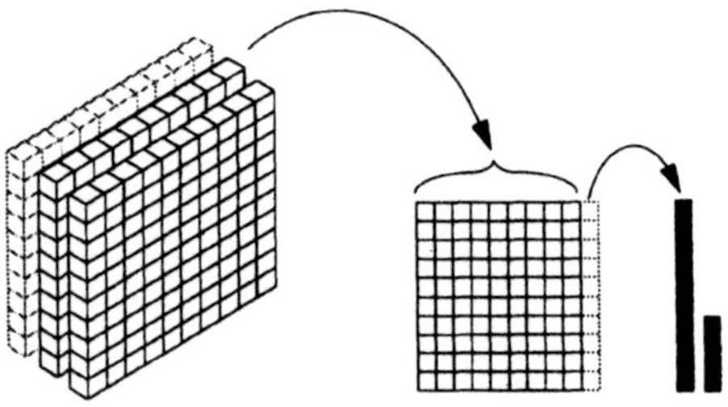

Carry back 1 hundred to the tens place.
Exchange 1 hundred for 10 tens.
Write a small 1 next to the 0.
Cross out the 3; write a 2 above the 3.
Carry back 1 ten to the ones place.
Write a small 1 next to the 4.
Cross out the 10; write a 9 above the 10.
Subtract the ones: 14 − 5 = 9.
Subtract the tens: 9 − 5 = 4.
Subtract the hundreds: 2 − 0 = 2.

```
  2  9
  3̸ 1̸0̸ ¹4
-     5  5
```

B

304 − 55	805 − 63	604 − 85	706 − 78	607 − 43
502 − 46	401 − 25	300 − 62	603 − 84	205 − 26

TEST

A Subtract.

624 − 82	748 − 85	502 − 99	443 − 76	629 − 45
204 − 175	802 − 578	637 − 365	357 − 173	723 − 58

B Add.

287 + 341	175 + 442	649 + 156	757 + 163	558 + 42
344 + 478	757 + 178	364 + 477	706 + 94	302 + 98

C

It is 332 miles from my home to Rutland, Vermont. If we stop for lunch after driving 208 miles, how many more miles must we drive?

Rob drove 158 miles to visit his grandfather. Then he drove 264 miles to Rutland. How many miles did Rob drive in all?

We must drive _____ more miles.

Rob drove _____ miles in all.

23

A

Thousands	Hundreds	Tens	Ones

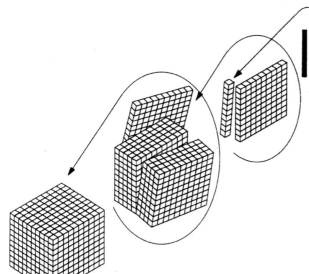

999 + 1 = ?

Add the ones: 9 + 1 = 10. You must regroup.
Exchange 10 ones for 1 ten.
Carry 1 ten to the tens place.
Add the tens: 9 + 1 = 10. You must regroup.
Exchange 10 tens for 1 hundred.
Carry 1 hundred to the hundreds place.
Add the hundreds: 9 + 1 = 10. You must regroup.
Exchange 10 hundreds for 1 thousand.
Carry 1 thousand to the thousands place.

B

999	665	804	773	591
+ 1	+ 345	+ 96	+ 227	+ 339

275	437	144	862	484
+ 125	+ 463	+ 876	+ 178	+ 336

384	217	543	673	388
+ 136	+ 793	+ 487	+ 357	+ 612

24

A

$$\begin{array}{r} {}^{8}\!\!\not{9}\,{}^{1}0\;5\;8 \\ -7\;1\;3\;4 \\ \hline 2\;4 \end{array}$$

Subtract the ones: 8 – 4 = 4.

Subtract the tens: 5 – 3 = 2.

Look at the hundreds.

You cannot take 1 hundred away from 0 hundreds.

You must regroup.

Carry back 1 thousand to the hundreds place.

Exchange 1 thousand for 10 hundreds.

Write a small 1 next to the 0.

Cross out the 9; write an 8 above the 9.

Subtract the hundreds: 10 – 1 = 9.

Subtract the thousands: 8 – 7 = 1.

B

9059 – 7138	7176 – 2934	3097 – 1466	5389 – 2653
1815 – 624	3209 – 3186	5267 – 5082	7428 – 7162
4208 – 1135	6576 – 494	7403 – 6172	8549 – 7474
4607 – 2488	2506 – 1358	8308 – 7139	8604 – 2357

A

We round numbers to make them easier to think about.

Round 16 to the nearest ten.

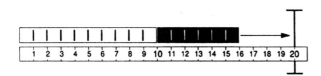

Look at the number 16. What is the digit in the ones place? _____ 6 is bigger than 5. When the number is 5 or bigger, you round to the nearest ten. You can see that 16 is closer to 20 than to 10, so you round 16 to 20.

Round to the nearest ten.

56 _____	45 _____	17 _____	76 _____
38 _____	27 _____	89 _____	55 _____
49 _____	68 _____	26 _____	18 _____

B

Round 12 to the nearest ten.

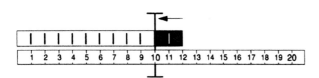

Look at the number 12. What is the digit in the ones place? _____
2 is smaller than 5, so you round it to the next lower ten. You can see that 12 is closer to 10 than to 20, so you round 12 to 10.

Round to the nearest ten.

82 _____	89 _____	66 _____	17 _____
94 _____	49 _____	64 _____	71 _____
73 _____	37 _____	25 _____	13 _____

A

Rounding to the nearest hundred

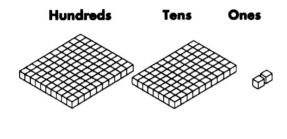

Hundreds	Tens	Ones

Round 182 to the nearest hundred.
Underline the number in the hundreds place.
Look at the number in the tens place.
8 is bigger than 5.
8 tens is closer to 1 hundred than to 1 ten, so
182 rounds to 200.

<u>1</u>   8   2

Round to the nearest hundred.

182 _____   739 _____   663 _____

401 _____   880 _____   209 _____

564 _____   919 _____   399 _____

B

Rounding to the nearest thousand

Thousands	Hundreds	Tens	Ones

Round 1725 to the nearest thousand.
Underline the number in the thousands place.
Look at the number in the hundreds place.
7 is bigger than 5.
7 hundreds is closer to 1 thousand than to
1 hundred, so 1725 rounds to 2000.

<u>1</u>   7   2   5

Round to the nearest thousand.

1725 _____   2834 _____   8465 _____

3859 _____   5328 _____   7199 _____

6249 _____   4710 _____   9448 _____

1

There are 1,000 students in South Side School. If 526 are girls, how many are boys?

_____ are boys.

2

The bookstore has 458 children's books. It ordered 268 more books. How many books will it have in all?

It will have _____ books in all.

3

The children want to raise $600 at the book fair. The first day they raised $329. How much more do they need to raise?

They need $_____ more.

4

There were 828 cars in the parking lot. After 4 o'clock there were 457 cars. How many had left?

_____ cars had left.

5

Carlotta drove 573 miles on Monday and 266 miles on Tuesday. How many miles did she drive?

She drove _____ miles.

6

There are 604 animals in the zoo. 135 are roaming free on an island. The rest are in cages. How many are in cages?

_____ animals are in cages.

7

From York to Albany it is 172 miles. From York to Rochester it is 230 miles. How far is it from Albany to Rochester?

_____ miles

8

Of the 135 children who came to the fair, 56 left early. The rest stayed until the end. How many stayed until the end?

_____ children stayed until the end.

TEST

A
Add.

| 464 | 677 | 744 | 832 | 975 |
| + 243 | + 332 | + 265 | + 177 | + 125 |

| 655 | 346 | 166 | 283 | 242 |
| + 345 | + 664 | + 834 | + 717 | + 758 |

B
Subtract.

| 324 | 270 | 643 | 1064 | 702 |
| − 264 | − 188 | − 354 | − 175 | − 437 |

| 470 | 367 | 1072 | 1043 | 802 |
| − 265 | − 278 | − 283 | − 384 | − 365 |

C
Round to the nearest ten.

37 _____   31 _____   42 _____   61 _____

68 _____   89 _____   77 _____   92 _____

Round to the nearest hundred.

264 _____   381 _____   342 _____   429 _____

A

1 dollar and 25 cents is worth 125 cents.
It is written $1.25.

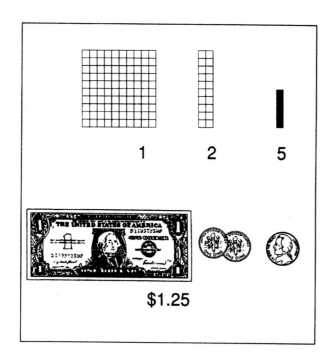

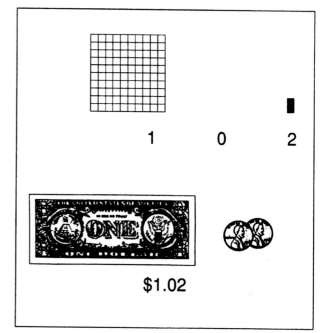

$1.25

$1.02

B

Fill in the blanks.

$9.85 = 9 dollars and 85 cents

$ 1.10 = _____ dollar and _____ cents

$4.30 = _____ dollars and _____ cents

$12.02 = _____ dollars and _____ cents

$2.05 = _____ dollars and _____ cents

$31.57 = _____ dollars and _____ cents

5 dollars and 68 cents = ___$5.68___

6 dollars and 50 cents = _____

7 dollars and 35 cents = _____

6 dollars and 5 cents = _____

3 dollars and 9 cents = _____

10 dollars = _____

2 dollars and 98 cents = _____

9 dollars and 25 cents = _____

4 dollars and 3 cents = _____

3 dollars = _____

A

Add these coins.

Think how much each coin is worth.

Write only the sum as you add one coin after the other.

<u> 25 </u>   <u> 35 </u>   <u>   </u>   <u>   </u>¢

<u>   </u>   <u>   </u>   <u>   </u>   <u>   </u>   <u>   </u>¢

B

Add the dollar bill and the coins.

    $1.40

<u>   </u>

    $.

<u>   </u>

C

$3.26	$7.80	$6.30	$8.08	$5.50
+ 1.45	+ .63	+ 1.75	+ .39	+ 2.75
$	$	$	$	$

$9.29	$6.52	$7.79	$4.00	$8.90
− 3.16	− 1.27	− 2.81	− .50	− 6.72
$	$	$	$	$

31

1

Michael had 50¢. His uncle gave him a quarter. How much money did he have then?

Known		Unknown
money on hand	money received	sum

50	+	25	=	

Michael had _____¢ altogether.

2

Raj had 85¢. He bought food for his goldfish for 80¢. How much money did Raj have left?

Known		Unknown
money on hand	money spent	remainder

Raj had _____¢ left.

3

Betty had 95¢. She bought a toy clown for 85¢. How much did she have left?

Known		Unknown
money on hand	money spent	remainder

Betty had _____¢ left.

4

Jessica has 90¢. Her sister has 80¢. How much less money does her sister have than Jessica has?

Known		Unknown
larger amount	smaller amount	difference

Her sister has _____¢ less than Jessica.

5

Ashley had 70¢ and Tiffany had 90¢. How much less money did Ashley have than Tiffany had?

Known		Unknown
larger amount	smaller amount	difference

Ashley had _____¢ less than Tiffany had.

6

Patty had 3 dimes in her bank. She earned 20¢ more. How much money did Patty have then?

Known		Unknown
money on hand	money received	sum

Patty had _____¢.

1

The twins bought a can of dog food for $.59. They gave the clerk a one dollar bill. How much change did they get?

They got $_____ change.

2

Jeff needed a station for his toy trains. He took a five dollar bill to the store. The station cost $3.98. How much change did he get?

Jeff got $_____ change.

3

David got his mother a basket of red flowers for Mother's Day. It cost $2.78. He gave the clerk three dollars. How much change did he get?

David got $_____ change.

4

Aunt Alice bought Lisa a watch for $3.85. She paid for it with a five dollar bill. How much change did she get?

She got $_____ change.

5

John's mother went shopping for John's birthday party. She paid 79¢ for candles, 65¢ for hats, and 85¢ for ice cream. She gave the clerk $5.00. How much change did she get?

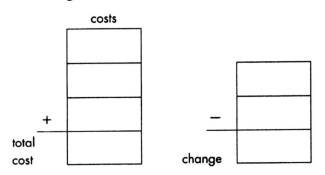

John's mother got $_____ change.

6

John's father spent $1.25 for prizes, $1.89 for paper cups, $2.00 for a table-cloth, and $2.95 for a game to play. He gave the clerk ten dollars. How much change did John's father get?

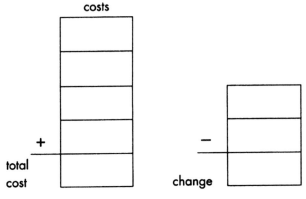

John's father got $_____ change.

33

A

What time is it?
The short hand tells the hour.
It is called the **hour hand**.

____ o'clock   ____ o'clock   ____ o'clock   ____ o'clock

B

Draw the hour hand on each clock.

   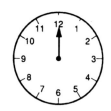

5 o'clock   1 o'clock   6 o'clock   9 o'clock

C

The long hand is called the **minute hand**.
The minute hands below show the quarters of the hour.

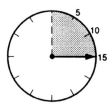 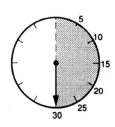 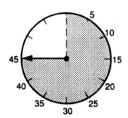 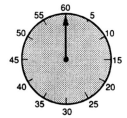

a quarter past   half past   a quarter of   on the hour

_____ minutes   _____ minutes   _____ minutes   _____ minutes
after the hour   after the hour   before the hour   one full hour

34

There is one full hour between 1 o'clock and 2 o'clock. The minute hand has gone around a full circle.

It is **1** o'clock.	This is one hour later.	It is **3** o'clock.	Show one hour later.
			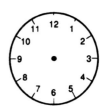
1:00	2:00	3:00	___:___

What time is it?	Show one hour later.	What time is it?	Show one hour later.
	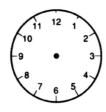		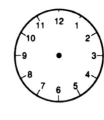
___:___	___:___	___:___	___:___

What time is it?	Show half an hour later.	What time is it?	Show half an hour later.
	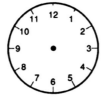		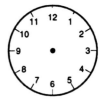
___:___	___:___	___:___	___:___

35

A

Minutes after the hour

Write: 10:05

Say: __5__ after 10

_____ : _____

_____ after 6

_____ : _____

_____ after _____

_____ : _____

_____ after _____

B

Minutes before the hour

Write: 2:55

Say: _____ of 3

_____ . _____

_____ of 6

_____ . _____

_____ of _____

_____ . _____

_____ of _____

C

Minutes after or before the hour

Write: 11:45

Say: a quarter of _____

_____ : _____

_____ after _____

_____ : _____

_____ of _____

_____ : _____

_____ after _____

1

Jim puts ice on his foot.

Jim hurt his foot. He has to put ice on it for a quarter of an hour. He puts the ice on his foot at **6:45**. When may he take it off?

Jim may take the ice off his foot at ____:____.

2

This is the time the train leaves.

The train to Boston leaves at **3:45**. Marion wants to be at the station **10** minutes before that. What time should Marion be at the station?

Marion should be at the station at ____:____.

3

This is the time the Browns left for the store.

The Browns went to the store. They left at **10** o'clock. They came home in **45** minutes. What time was it when they came home?

They came home at ____:____.

4

This is the time the party begins.

Melissa is going to Jennifer's birthday party. The party begins at **3** o'clock. It takes **5** minutes to get to Jennifer's house. What time should Melissa start?

Melissa should start at ____:____.

5

This is the time Daniel got to school.

Daniel got to school at **8:25**. He left his house **10** minutes before that. What time did Daniel leave his house?

Daniel left at ____:____.

A

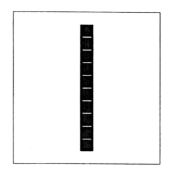

1 ten

When you draw 1 ten 4 times, you have 4 tens.

Draw 1 ten 3 times. You have ____ tens.

B

Math does not use words; it uses symbols and signs.

Say: "4 times 10 equals 40." Write: $4 \times 10 = 40$.

$2 \times 10 =$ ____ $6 \times 10 =$ ____ $5 \times 10 =$ ____

C

When you put 10-blocks in the track, you build a 10-scale.

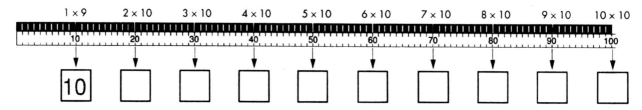

Write the multiples of 10 in the boxes.

D

Write the 10-table.

$1 \times 10 = 10$	6
$2 \times 10 =$	7
$3 \times$	8
4	9
5	10

38

A

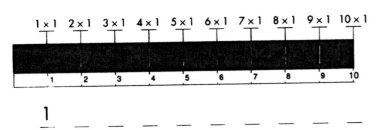

Write some facts from the **1**-table.

1 × 1 = _____

2 × 1 = _____

_____

_____

_____

_____

1 ___ ___ ___ ___ ___ ___ ___ ___ ___

There are **1**-blocks in this track.
Write the multiples of **1** on the lines.

B

The 2-Table

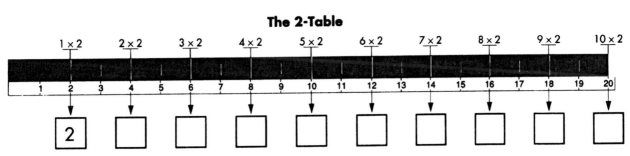

There are **2**-blocks in this track.
Write the multiples of **2** in the boxes.

C The multiples of **2** are even numbers.

 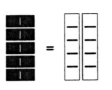 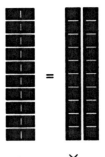

3 × 2 = $\underline{2 \times 3}$ 4 × 2 = $\underline{\quad \times \quad}$ 5 × 2 = $\underline{\quad \times \quad}$ 10 × 2 = $\underline{\quad \times \quad}$

D Write the 2-table.

1 × 2 = _____   6 _____

2 × 2 = _____   7 _____

3 _____   8 _____

4 _____   9 _____

5 _____   10 _____

THE 5-TABLE IN THE DUAL BOARD

Odd multiples of 5

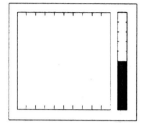

1 × 5 = 5

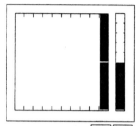

3 × 5 = 15

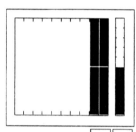

5 × 5 = ☐☐

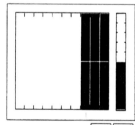

7 × 5 = ☐☐

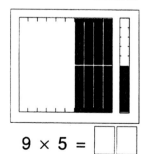

9 × 5 = ☐☐

Even multiples of 5

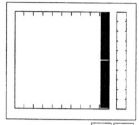

2 × 5 = 10

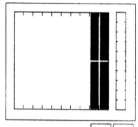

4 × 5 = ☐☐

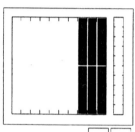

6 × 5 = ☐☐

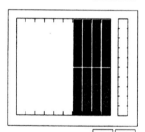

8 × 5 = ☐☐

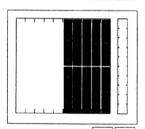

10 × 5 = ☐☐

A

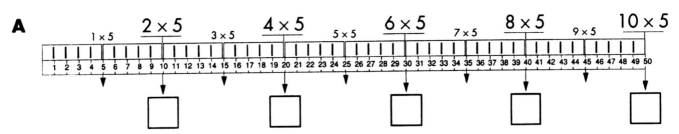

Write the even multiples of **5** in the boxes.
Two **5**-blocks fill each decade.

B

Write the
multiples of 10.

10									100

Each multiple
of **5** is half the
multiple of 10.

5									50

C

$\begin{array}{r} 5 \\ \times\ 3 \\ \hline \end{array}$ Say: "3 times 5."

$\begin{array}{r} 5 \\ \times\ 7 \\ \hline \end{array}$ $\begin{array}{r} 5 \\ \times\ 4 \\ \hline \end{array}$ $\begin{array}{r} 5 \\ \times\ 8 \\ \hline \end{array}$ $\begin{array}{r} 5 \\ \times\ 5 \\ \hline \end{array}$ $\begin{array}{r} 5 \\ \times\ 6 \\ \hline \end{array}$

$\begin{array}{r} 5 \\ \times\ 1 \\ \hline \end{array}$ $\begin{array}{r} 5 \\ \times\ 2 \\ \hline \end{array}$ $\begin{array}{r} 5 \\ \times\ 9 \\ \hline \end{array}$ $\begin{array}{r} 5 \\ \times\ 10 \\ \hline \end{array}$ $\begin{array}{r} 5 \\ \times\ 3 \\ \hline \end{array}$

D

Write the 5-table.

$1 \times 5 = 5$

$2 \times 5 =$

41

A

The 9-table in the number track

$1 \times 10 = 10$

$1 \times 9 = 10 - 1$

$1 \times 9 = \underline{\hspace{2em}}$

2×10 is 20,

but 2×9 is $20 - 2$.

$2 \times 9 = \underline{\hspace{2em}}$

3×10 is 30,

but 3×9 is $30 - 3$.

$3 \times 9 = \underline{\hspace{2em}}$

B

Cross out what you subtract. Fill in the blanks.

$4 \times 10 = \underline{\hspace{2em}}$,

so 4×9 can't be 40.

$4 \times 9 = 40 - 4$

$4 \times 9 = \underline{\hspace{2em}}$

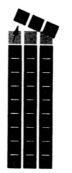

$5 \times 10 = \underline{\hspace{2em}}$,

so 5×9 can't be 50.

$5 \times 9 = 50 - 5$

$5 \times 9 = \underline{\hspace{2em}}$

$6 \times 10 = \underline{\hspace{2em}}$

$6 \times 9 = 60 - \underline{\hspace{2em}}$

$6 \times 9 = \underline{\hspace{2em}}$

$7 \times 10 = \underline{\hspace{2em}}$

$7 \times 9 = 70 - \underline{\hspace{2em}}$

$7 \times 9 = \underline{\hspace{2em}}$

$8 \times 10 = \underline{\hspace{2em}}$

$8 \times 9 = 80 - \underline{\hspace{2em}}$

$8 \times 9 = \underline{\hspace{2em}}$

$9 \times 10 = \underline{\hspace{2em}}$

$9 \times 9 = 90 - \underline{\hspace{2em}}$

$9 \times 9 = \underline{\hspace{2em}}$

The answer to a multiplication example is called the **product**.

In the 9-table, the digits of each product add up to 9.

Look at 2×9.
2 nines are 18.
Look at the digits of the product 18.
The digits are 1 and 8. 1 and 8 add up to 9.

---

3 nines = how many tens and ones?

Take 1 nine;
put it on top.

Break it into 2 and 7.

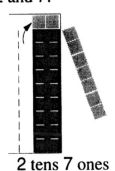

3 nines =   2 tens 7 ones

$$3 \times 9 = \boxed{2}\ \boxed{7}$$

Add the digits: $2 + 7 =$ ____

$4 \times 9 = ?$

Take 1 nine;
put it on top.

Break it into 3 and 6.

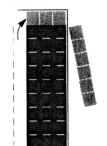

4 nines =   3 tens 6 ones

$$4 \times 9 = \boxed{}\ \boxed{}$$

Add the digits: $3 + 6 =$ ____

$5 \times 9 = ?$

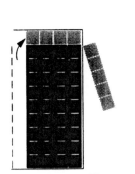

5 nines =   4 tens 5 ones

$$5 \times 9 = \boxed{}\ \boxed{}$$

$6 \times 9 = ?$

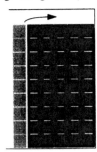
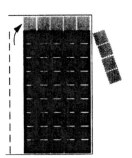

6 nines =   5 tens 4 ones

$$6 \times 9 = \boxed{}\ \boxed{}$$

tens   ones

$7 \times 9 = \boxed{} + \boxed{}$ or _____

$8 \times 9 = \boxed{} + \boxed{}$ or _____

tens   ones

$9 \times 9 = \boxed{} + \boxed{}$ or _____

$10 \times 9 = \boxed{} + \boxed{}$ or _____

THE 9-TABLE

A

Write the multiples of 9 in the boxes.

| 1×9 | 2×9 | 3×9 | 4×9 | 5×9 | 6×9 | 7×9 | 8×9 | 9×9 | 10×9 |

Think: The digits of each multiple of 9 add up to 9.

B

Write the multiple of 9 that comes in each decade.

	Tens	Ones				Tens	Ones	
in the thirties	3	6	_4_ × 9	in the twenties			___ × 9
in the sixties			___ × 9	in the forties			___ × 9
in the fifties			___ × 9	in the seventies			___ × 9
in the eighties			___ × 9	in the nineties			___ × 9
in the teens			___ × 9

C

Write the multiples of 9.

| 9 | 18 | | | | | | | | |

D

Write the 9-table.

$1 \times 9 = 9$

_____

_____

_____

_____

_____

_____

_____

_____

A

Multiply.

1	9	9	2	5	10	5	1
× 2	× 9	× 3	× 2	× 8	× 10	× 1	× 10

5	10	2	9	5	10	9	2
× 2	× 9	× 3	× 8	× 9	× 2	× 7	× 4

B

$6 \times 2 =$ _____ $5 \times 1 =$ _____ $9 \times 9 =$ _____

$5 \times 10 =$ _____ $10 \times 10 =$ _____ $1 \times 1 =$ _____

$6 \times 9 =$ _____ $7 \times 9 =$ _____ $8 \times 2 =$ _____

$1 \times 10 =$ _____ $3 \times 10 =$ _____ $4 \times 9 =$ _____

$10 \times 9 =$ _____ $7 \times 5 =$ _____ $8 \times 9 =$ _____

C

5	10	1	10	2	5	1	5
× 3	× 8	× 3	× 7	× 9	× 10	× 4	× 4

9	2	5	10	2	5	1	9
× 2	× 5	× 7	× 6	× 10	× 5	× 6	× 4

9	2	9	10	5	9	9	1
× 6	× 7	× 5	× 4	× 6	× 1	× 5	× 8

A

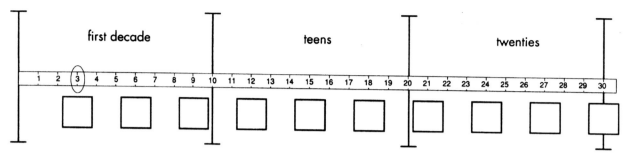

Draw a line around the multiples of 3 on the number track.
Write the multiples of 3 in the boxes.

How many multiples of 3 are in each decade? _____ The first multiple is 1 × 3 = _____.

The last multiple is 10 × 3 = _____.

B

$$\begin{array}{r} 3 \\ \times\ 5 \\ \hline \end{array}$$ Say: "5 times 3."

$$\begin{array}{r} 3 \\ \times\ 2 \\ \hline \end{array}$$

$$\begin{array}{r} 3 \\ \times\ 3 \\ \hline \end{array}$$

$$\begin{array}{r} 3 \\ \times\ 6 \\ \hline \end{array}$$

$$\begin{array}{r} 3 \\ \times\ 8 \\ \hline \end{array}$$

$$\begin{array}{r} 3 \\ \times\ 1 \\ \hline \end{array}$$

$$\begin{array}{r} 3 \\ \times\ 7 \\ \hline \end{array}$$

$$\begin{array}{r} 3 \\ \times\ 10 \\ \hline \end{array}$$

$$\begin{array}{r} 3 \\ \times\ 4 \\ \hline \end{array}$$

$$\begin{array}{r} 3 \\ \times\ 2 \\ \hline \end{array}$$

$$\begin{array}{r} 3 \\ \times\ 9 \\ \hline \end{array}$$

C

Write the multiples of 3.

3 □ □ □ □ □ □ □ □ □

D

Write the 3-table.   1 × 3 = 3

_____   _____

_____   _____

_____   _____

_____   _____

_____   _____

46

A

Doubling something means to produce it twice.

1 three   1 × 3 = ____

2 threes   2 × 3 = ____

Double the 2 threes.

2 threes	6	
+ 2 threes	+ 6	
4 threes =	12	6 + 6

4 × 3 = ____

Double the 4 threes.

4 threes	12	
+ 4 threes	+ 12	
8 threes =	____	12 + 12

8 × 3 = ____

B

Double the 3 threes.

3 threes =	?	

3 × 3 = ____

3 threes	9	
+ 3 threes	+ 9	
____ threes =	____	9 + 9

6 × 3 = ____

C

Solve for *X*.

$X = 2 \times 3$ $X = 4 \times 3$ $X = 3 \times 3$

$X =$ ____ $X =$ ____ $X =$ ____

$X = 4 \times 3$ $X = 8 \times 3$ $X = 6 \times 3$

$X =$ ____ $X =$ ____ $X =$ ____

47

THE 4-TABLE

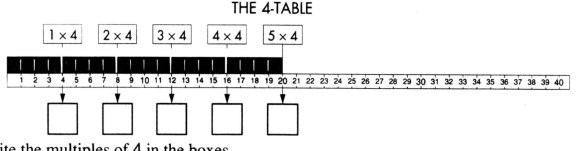

Write the multiples of 4 in the boxes.

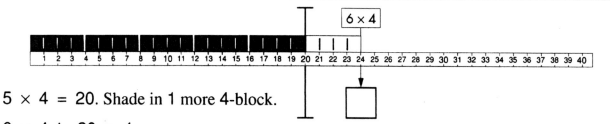

5 × 4 = 20. Shade in 1 more 4-block.

6 × 4 is 20 + 4.

6 × 4 = _____. Write it in the box.

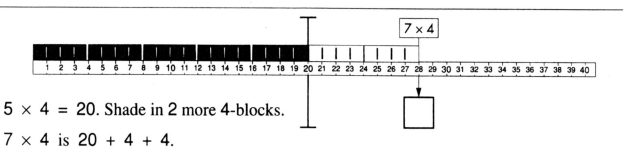

5 × 4 = 20. Shade in 2 more 4-blocks.

7 × 4 is 20 + 4 + 4.

7 × 4 = _____. Write it in the box.

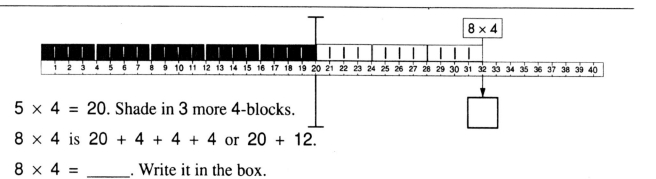

5 × 4 = 20. Shade in 3 more 4-blocks.

8 × 4 is 20 + 4 + 4 + 4 or 20 + 12.

8 × 4 = _____. Write it in the box.

10 × 4 = _____.

9 × 4 = 40 − 4

9 × 4 = _____.

48

THE 4-TABLE

A

| first decade | teens | twenties | thirties |

1 2 3 4 5 6 7 8 9 10 11 12 13 14 15 16 17 18 19 20 21 22 23 24 25 26 27 28 29 30 31 32 33 34 35 36 37 38 39 40

Draw a line around the multiples of 4 on the number track.

Write the multiples of 4 in the boxes.

The first multiple is $1 \times 4 =$ _____.

The last multiple is $10 \times 4 =$ _____.

B

Write the
multiples of 2.

| 2 | | | | | | | | | 20 |

Double each
one to get the
multiples of 4.

| 4 | | | | | | | | | 40 |

C

$$
\begin{array}{ccccc}
4 & 4 & 4 & 4 & 4 \\
\times\ 5 & \times\ 1 & \times\ 9 & \times\ 3 & \times\ 10
\end{array}
$$

$$
\begin{array}{ccccc}
4 & 4 & 4 & 4 & 4 \\
\times\ 6 & \times\ 2 & \times\ 4 & \times\ 7 & \times\ 8
\end{array}
$$

D Write the 4-table.

$1 \times 4 =$ _____   _____

_____   _____

_____   _____

_____   _____

_____   _____

49

A

10 fours = 4 tens   10 twos = 2 tens   10 threes = 3 tens

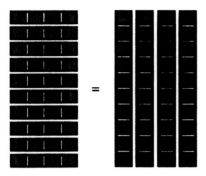   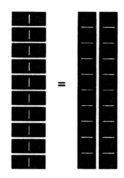   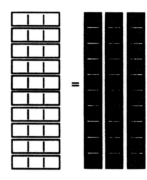

$10 \times 4 = 4 \times 10$ $10 \times 2 = 2 \times 10$ $10 \times 3 = 3 \times 10$

$10 \times 4 =$ _____ $10 \times 2 =$ _____ $10 \times 3 =$ _____

B   Write the tenth multiple of each table.

$10 \times 3 = 3 \times 10$ __30__ $10 \times 6 = 6 \times 10$ _____

$10 \times 4 = 4 \times 10$ _____ $10 \times 5 = 5 \times 10$ _____

$10 \times 7 = 7 \times 10$ _____ $10 \times 9 = 9 \times 10$ _____

C

0-Facts

Think of the 5-block when you read these equations:

$5 + 0$ means you have **5** and no other block. $5 + 0 =$ _____.

$5 - 0$ means you take nothing away. $5 - 0 =$ _____.

5×0 means you have **5** times nothing.
        Do you have anything? $5 \times 0 =$ _____.

0×5 means do not take the 5-block!
        Do you have anything? $0 \times 5 =$ _____.

$3 + 0 =$ _____ $3 \times 0 =$ _____ $8 + 0 =$ _____

$4 - 0 =$ _____ $0 \times 4 =$ _____ $0 + 2 =$ _____

$6 + 0 =$ _____ $6 \times 0 =$ _____ $0 \times 2 =$ _____

50

TEST

A

Multiply.

3	5	4	9	3	9	4	3
× 0	× 3	× 7	× 3	× 1	× 4	× 6	× 3

3	1	5	4	9	3	5	4
× 2	× 0	× 5	× 5	× 6	× 10	× 9	× 4

B

5 × 4 = _____   5 × 0 = _____   3 × 9 = _____

10 × 4 = _____   8 × 2 = _____   4 × 4 = _____

7 × 3 = _____   10 × 5 = _____   8 × 3 = _____

3 × 4 = _____   5 × 9 = _____   6 × 4 = _____

0 × 10 = _____   7 × 4 = _____   8 × 4 = _____

C

4	6	3	9	4	7	3	9
× 8	× 0	× 5	× 9	× 2	× 0	× 6	× 8

5	3	9	8	4	3	2	3
× 6	× 7	× 6	× 0	× 1	× 8	× 9	× 4

5	3	5	9	5	9	10	4
× 8	× 9	× 0	× 7	× 7	× 0	× 10	× 9

51

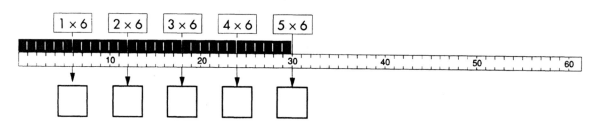

Write the multiples of 6 in the boxes.

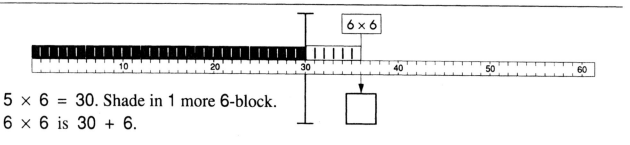

5 × 6 = 30. Shade in 1 more 6-block.
6 × 6 is 30 + 6.

6 × 6 = _____. Write it in the box.

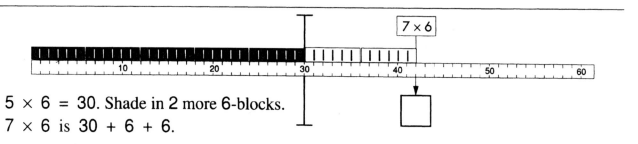

5 × 6 = 30. Shade in 2 more 6-blocks.
7 × 6 is 30 + 6 + 6.

7 × 6 = _____. Write it in the box.

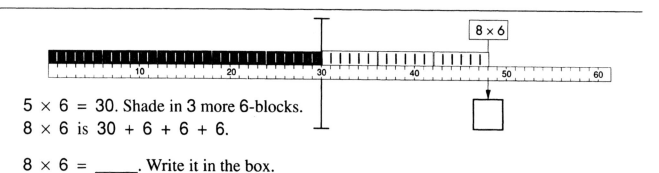

5 × 6 = 30. Shade in 3 more 6-blocks.
8 × 6 is 30 + 6 + 6 + 6.

8 × 6 = _____. Write it in the box.

10 × 6 = _____ This is the last multiple.
 9 × 6 = 60 − 6

 9 × 6 = _____

A

first decade	teens	twenties	thirties	forties	fifties

1×6 $\quad$ 2×6 $\quad$ 3×6 $\quad$ 4×6 $\quad$ 5×6 $\quad$ 6×6 $\quad$ 7×6 $\quad$ 8×6 $\quad$ 9×6 $\quad$ 10×6

Write the multiples of 6 in the boxes.

The first multiple is $1 \times 6 =$ _____.

The last multiple is $10 \times 6 =$ _____.

B

Write the multiples of 3.

3									30

Double each one to get the multiples of 6.

6									60

C

$$\begin{array}{r} 6 \\ \times\ 5 \\ \hline \end{array} \qquad \begin{array}{r} 6 \\ \times\ 10 \\ \hline \end{array} \qquad \begin{array}{r} 6 \\ \times\ 9 \\ \hline \end{array} \qquad \begin{array}{r} 6 \\ \times\ 3 \\ \hline \end{array} \qquad \begin{array}{r} 6 \\ \times\ 1 \\ \hline \end{array}$$

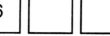

$$\begin{array}{r} 6 \\ \times\ 7 \\ \hline \end{array} \qquad \begin{array}{r} 6 \\ \times\ 2 \\ \hline \end{array} \qquad \begin{array}{r} 6 \\ \times\ 6 \\ \hline \end{array} \qquad \begin{array}{r} 6 \\ \times\ 8 \\ \hline \end{array} \qquad \begin{array}{r} 6 \\ \times\ 4 \\ \hline \end{array}$$

D

Write the 6-table.

$1 \times 6 =$ _____ _____

_____ _____

_____ _____

_____ _____

_____ _____

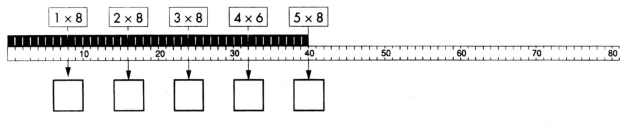

Write the multiples of **8** in the boxes.

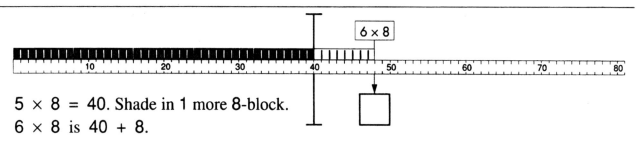

$5 \times 8 = 40$. Shade in 1 more 8-block.

6×8 is $40 + 8$.

$6 \times 8 =$ _____. Write it in the box.

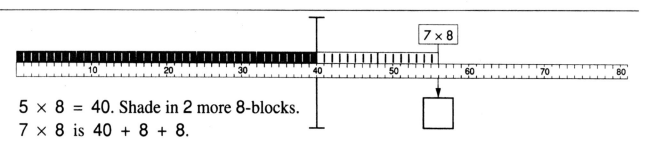

$5 \times 8 = 40$. Shade in 2 more 8-blocks.

7×8 is $40 + 8 + 8$.

$7 \times 8 =$ _____. Write it in the box.

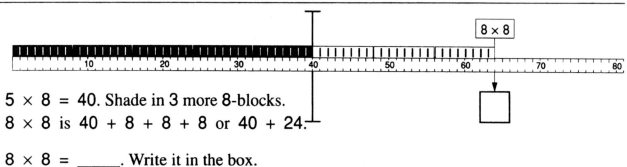

$5 \times 8 = 40$. Shade in 3 more 8-blocks.

8×8 is $40 + 8 + 8 + 8$ or $40 + 24$.

$8 \times 8 =$ _____. Write it in the box.

$10 \times 8 =$ _____

$9 \times 8 = 80 - 8$

$9 \times 8 =$ _____

THE 8-TABLE

A

first decade | teens | twenties | thirties | forties | fifties | sixties | seventies

1×8 | 2×8 | 3×8 | 4×8 | 5×8 | 6×8 | 7×8 | 8×8 | 9×8 | 10×8

Write the multiples of 8 in the boxes.

The first multiple is $1 \times 8 =$ _____.

The last multiple is $10 \times 8 =$ _____.

B

Write the multiples of 4.

4									

Double each one to get the multiples of 8.

8									

C

8	8	8	8	8
× 5	× 6	× 3	× 2	× 4

8	8	8	8	8
× 1	× 10	× 9	× 8	× 7

D

Write the 8-table.

$1 \times 8 =$ _____   _____

_____   _____

_____   _____

_____   _____

_____   _____

A

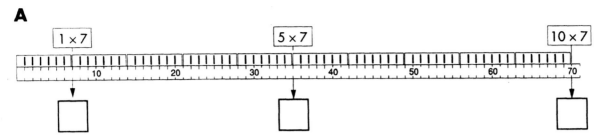

Write the first and last multiples in the boxes.

What is the multiple in the middle?

5×7 is half of 70.

$5 \times 7 =$ _____. Write it in the box.

B

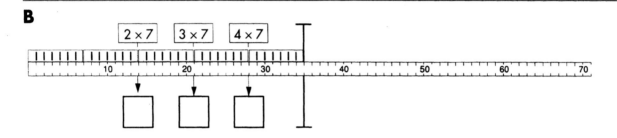

These are the multiples just before the middle.

Write them in the boxes.

C

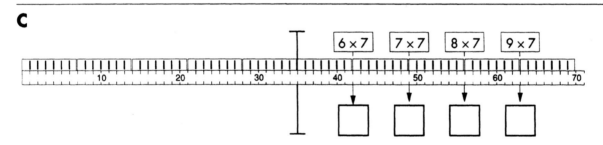

These are the multiples after the middle.

Write them in the boxes.

D

Write the multiples of 7.

7									

THE 7-TABLE

A

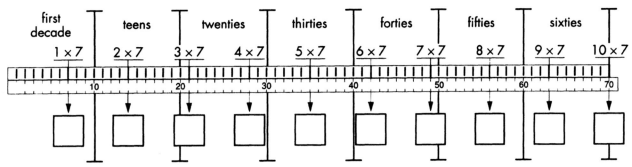

Write the multiples of 7 in the boxes.

The first multiple is 1 × 7 = _____.

The last multiple is 10 × 7 = _____.

B

Write the multiples of 7.

in the first decade _____

in the teens _____

in the twenties _____, _____

in the thirties _____

in the forties _____, _____

in the fifties _____

in the sixties _____

in the seventies _____

C

```
    7          7          7          7          7
  × 5       × 10       ×  9       ×  3       ×  1
 ____       ____       ____       ____       ____


    7          7          7          7          7
  × 7       ×  8       ×  6       ×  2       ×  4
 ____       ____       ____       ____       ____
```

D Write the 7-table.   1 × 7 = _____   _____

_____   _____

_____   _____

_____   _____

_____   _____

A

Common multiples are multiples that several tables have in common. Look at the number track.

Which multiples do the 3-table and the 6-table have in common?

The 3-table and the 6-table have these multiples in common:

__6__, __12__, _____, _____, _____.

B

Draw a line around the multiples of 3 on the number track below.
Draw a line around the multiples of 4 in a different color.

The 3-table and the 4-table have these multiples in common: _____, _____.

C

Draw a line around the multiples of 2 on the number track below.
Draw a line around the multiples of 4 in a different color.

The 2-table and the 4-table have these multiples in common:

_____, _____, _____, _____, _____, _____, _____.

58

A

Multiply.

6	7	9	7	6	7	8	4
× 1	× 8	× 4	× 0	× 8	× 1	× 10	× 4

3	7	8	8	3	7	6	7
× 7	× 6	× 9	× 0	× 8	× 7	× 3	× 8

B

$6 \times 3 =$ _____ $8 \times 8 =$ _____ $7 \times 7 =$ _____

$4 \times 6 =$ _____ $6 \times 4 =$ _____ $8 \times 6 =$ _____

$6 \times 7 =$ _____ $9 \times 7 =$ _____ $7 \times 6 =$ _____

$2 \times 8 =$ _____ $4 \times 8 =$ _____ $1 \times 8 =$ _____

$5 \times 6 =$ _____ $2 \times 6 =$ _____ $7 \times 8 =$ _____

C

8	7	4	7	6	5	8	4
× 6	× 4	× 6	× 10	× 6	× 8	× 3	× 7

5	6	9	8	8	7	9	7
× 7	× 7	× 3	× 5	× 7	× 3	× 7	× 5

8	8	6	7	8	9	10	7
× 8	× 4	× 9	× 2	× 6	× 8	× 9	× 4

A

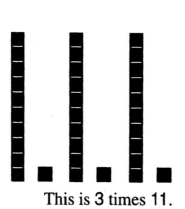

This is 11.

This is 3 times 11.

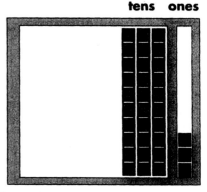

tens ones

$3 \times 11 = 3$ tens $+ 3$ ones

$3 \times 11 = \boxed{}$

B

$2 \times 11 =$ _____ $3 \times 11 =$ _____

$4 \times 11 =$ _____ $7 \times 11 =$ _____

$9 \times 11 =$ _____ $5 \times 11 =$ _____

$6 \times 11 =$ _____ $8 \times 11 =$ _____

C

Can you see how **10 elevens** become **11 tens**?

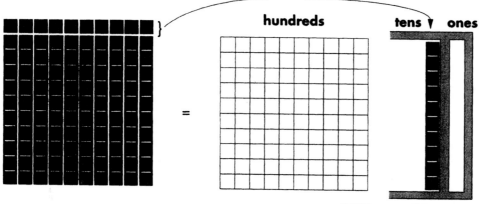

hundreds   tens   ones

10×11 makes $\boxed{1}$ $\boxed{1}$ $\boxed{0}$ $10 \times 11 =$ ___

D

Write the multiples of 11.

11	22								110

 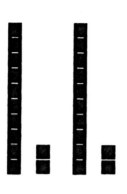

This is 12.   This is 2 times 12.

$3 \times 12 = 3$ tens $+ 3$ twos

$3 \times 12 = $ [|]

$4 \times 12 = 4$ tens $+ 4$ twos

$4 \times 12 = $ _____ $+$ _____

$4 \times 12 = $ _____

$8 \times 12 = 8$ tens $+ 8$ twos

$8 \times 12 = $ _____ $+$ _____

$8 \times 12 = $ _____

$5 \times 12 = 5$ tens $+ 5$ twos

$5 \times 12 = $ _____ $+$ _____

$5 \times 12 = $ _____

$9 \times 12 = 9$ tens $+ 9$ twos

$9 \times 12 = $ _____ $+$ _____

$9 \times 12 = $ _____

$6 \times 12 = 6$ tens $+ 6$ twos

$6 \times 12 = $ _____ $+$ _____

$6 \times 12 = $ _____

$10 \times 12 = 10$ tens $+ 10$ twos

$10 \times 12 = $ _____ $+$ _____

$10 \times 12 = $ _____

$7 \times 12 = 7$ tens $+ 7$ twos

$7 \times 12 = $ _____ $+$ _____

$7 \times 12 = $ _____

1 dozen eggs $= 12$ eggs

2 dozen eggs $= 2 \times 12$ eggs

2 dozen eggs $= $ _____ eggs

3 dozen eggs $= 3 \times 12$ eggs

3 dozen eggs $= $ _____ eggs

1

The tailor bought 5 cards of buttons. There were 6 buttons on each card. How many buttons did the tailor buy?

1 card has _____ buttons.

5 cards have _____ × _____ buttons,

so 5 cards have _____ buttons.

The tailor bought _____ buttons.

2

The teacher had 6 boxes of crayons. There were 10 crayons in each box. How many crayons were there?

1 box had _____ crayons.

6 boxes had _____ × _____ crayons,

so 6 boxes had _____ crayons.

There were _____ crayons.

3

In the art class 5 children are making wagons. Each wagon needs 4 wheels. How many wheels should the teacher buy?

The teacher should buy _____ wheels.

4

The second grade took a trip. 4 children rode in each car. There were 5 cars in all. How many children went on the trip?

_____ children went on the trip.

5

Mr. Winn will bake bran muffins for the school fair. Each pan makes 6 muffins. If he bakes 4 pans, how many bran muffins will he take to the fair?

Mr. Winn will take _____ muffins to the fair.

6

Sally and 5 friends went to the bookstore. Each of the 6 girls bought 3 books. How many books did they buy altogether?

The girls bought _____ books altogether.

62

10¢ each

1 orange costs _____10_ ¢.

8 oranges cost __8__ × _____ ¢,

so 8 oranges cost _____ ¢.

1

At 9¢ apiece, what is the price of 7 pears?

1 pear costs _____ ¢.

7 pears cost _____ × _____ ¢.

so 7 pears cost _____ ¢.

2

At 12¢ each, how much will 4 bananas cost?

1 banana costs _____ ¢.

4 bananas cost _____ × _____ ¢,

so 4 bananas cost _____ ¢.

3

When Tom was in Portland, he got 8 picture postcards. Now he wants to buy 12¢ stamps for them. How much money does he need for the stamps?

Tom needs _____ ¢ for the stamps.

4

The price of one nail is 6¢. How much do a dozen nails cost?

A dozen nails cost _____ ¢.

5

The children want to stick little toy flags into their sand castle. Each flag costs 4¢. They want to buy 8 flags. How much will they pay for 8 flags?

The children will pay _____ ¢.

6

There are 7 children in the sports club. Each child will give the club $3. How much money will the club get from them?

The club will get $_____.

The children built a playhouse 4 feet high. The tree next to it is 3 times as high as the playhouse. How high is the tree?

3 × _____ = _____

The tree is _____ feet tall.

1

Julio got a pen for one dollar. He paid 4 times as much for a special notebook. How much did the notebook cost?

The notebook cost _____ dollars.

2

Bob did his homework in 10 minutes. His sister took three times as long to do hers. How long did it take her?

It took Bob's sister _____ minutes.

3

Jo's dog weighs 20 pounds. Jo weighs four times as much as her dog. How much does Jo weigh?

Jo weighs _____ pounds.

4

The twins are 2 years old. Ann is 8 times as old as the twins. How old is Ann?

Ann is _____ years old.

5

The pond is 2 feet deep at one end. In the middle it is 4 times as deep. How deep is the middle of the pond?

The middle of the pond is _____ feet deep.

6

Andrew lives 1 mile from school. His friend lives twice as far from school. How far does his friend live from school?

Andrew's friend lives _____ miles from school.

1

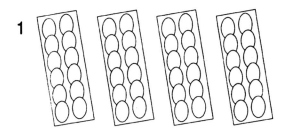

The bakery ordered 4 dozen eggs. How many eggs did it order?

Will you multiply or add to find the answer? Draw a line around the word.

multiply   add

4 × 12 =

The bakery ordered _____ eggs.

2

S	M	T	W	T	F	S	
X	X	X	X	X	X	X	
X	X	X	X	X	X	X	} England
X	X	X	X	X	X	X	
X	X	X	X	X	X	X	} France

Janet went to England for 3 weeks and to France for 1 week. How many weeks did her trip last?

Will you multiply or add to find the answer? Draw a line around the word.

multiply   add

Janet's trip lasted _____ weeks.

3

Christopher and his friends had a picnic. There were 8 boys. Each boy brought 3 sandwiches. How many sandwiches did they bring altogether?

Will you multiply or add to find the answer? Draw a line around the word.

multiply   add

The boys brought _____ sandwiches altogether.

4

To get to her office Mom must drive 6 miles to the station. If the train ride is 12 miles, how far does Mom travel to get to her office?

Will you multiply or add to find the answer? Draw a line around the word.

multiply   add

Mom travels _____ miles to her office.

5

Latoya is 9 years old. Ahmed is 3 times as old as Latoya. How old is Ahmed?

Will you multiply or add to find the answer? Draw a line around the word.

multiply   add

Ahmed is _____ years old.

6

Rex wants to bring 2 apples for each boy in his club. There are 8 boys in the club. How many apples must Rex bring?

Will you multiply or add to find the answer? Draw a line around the word.

multiply   add

Rex must bring _____ apples.

1

When Kevin became ill, the doctor told his mother to give him 4 glasses of juice a day for 3 days. How many glasses of juice did Kevin drink in all?

Will you multiply or add to find the answer? Draw a line around the word.

multiply   add

Kevin drank _____ glasses of juice.

2

Mrs. Jones invited each child on her block to have a bag of popcorn. There were 11 boys and 13 girls. How many bags of popcorn did she buy?

Will you multiply or add to find the answer? Draw a line around the word.

multiply   add

Mrs. Jones bought _____ bags of popcorn.

3

Jane bought 5 red balloons and 4 blue balloons for her party. How many balloons did she buy altogether?

Will you multiply or add to find the answer? Draw a line around the word.

multiply   add

Jane bought _____ balloons altogether.

4

The third-grade class went to the zoo in 6 cars. There were 5 children in each car. How many children went to the zoo?

Will you multiply or add to find the answer? Draw a line around the word.

multiply   add

_____ children went to the zoo.

5

The librarian brought 8 books on travel and 12 books on animals to put on the reading table. How many books did he put on the reading table?

Will you multiply or add to find the answer? Draw a line around the word.

multiply   add

The librarian put _____ books on the reading table.

6

On Monday Amanda bought 6 oranges. On Wednesday she bought twice as many. How many oranges did Amanda buy on Wednesday?

Will you multiply or add to find the answer? Draw a line around the word.

multiply   add

Amanda bought _____ oranges on Wednesday.

A

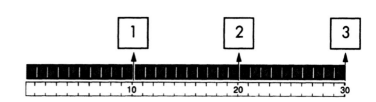

These are 3 10-blocks.   These 10-blocks reach 30 in the number track.

You have 3 10-blocks.   You know the 10-blocks reach 30.

Ask: How much is 3 times 10?   Ask: How many 10s are in 30?

Multiply to find the product.   Divide to find how many 10s in 30.

Write: 3 × 10 = _____   Write: 10) 30

B

How many 10's   Find 20 in the track.   Write the answer above it.   10) 20
are in 20?   20 is the **dividend**.   The answer is the **quotient**.

10 is the **divisor**.

C

2
10) 20   10) 50   10) 60   10) 70   10) 40

10) 80   10) 30   10) 90   10) 10   10)100

D

José has 80 pennies in his bank. If he   Shawn is painting toys for the fair.
puts them in piles of 10, how many piles   If it takes 10 minutes to paint one toy,
can he make?   how many toys can Shawn paint in 30
Think: One pile has 10 pennies.   minutes?
Ask: How many 10s in 80?   Think: One toy takes 10 minutes.
                                               Ask: How many 10s in 30?

10) 80   10) 30

José can make _____ piles of pennies.   Shawn can paint _____ toys in 30
                                               minutes.

67

A

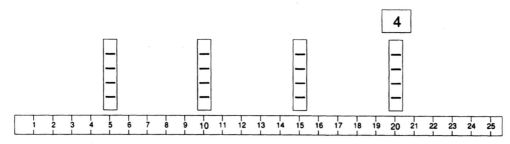

This is a multiplication fact:	Ask: "How many 5s are in 20?"	Write the division fact like this:
4 × 5 = _____		5) $\overline{20}$

| When you know the multiplication fact, it is easy to write the answer to the division example. | **multiplication**
2 × 5 = _____

3 × 5 = _____

6 × 5 = _____ | **division**
5) $\overline{10}$

5) $\overline{15}$

5) $\overline{30}$ |

B

5) $\overline{35}$ 5) $\overline{45}$ 5) $\overline{25}$ 5) $\overline{20}$ 5) $\overline{50}$

5) $\overline{10}$ 5) $\overline{30}$ 5) $\overline{40}$ 5) $\overline{15}$ 5) $\overline{5}$

C

Each child needs **5** crayons. The teacher has **20** crayons. How many children can get a set of **5** crayons?

Think: Each child gets 5 crayons.
Ask: How many groups of 5 are in 20?

Draw a line around each group of **5** crayons in the picture above.

You have found how many 5s are in 20. Write the example:

_____ children can get a set of crayons.

68

DIVISION: THE 2-TABLE AND THE 1-TABLE

A

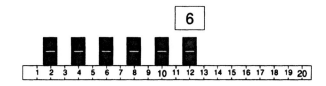

multiplication	**division**
Ask: How much is 6 times 2?	Ask: How many 2s are in 12?
Write: _____ × _____ = _____	Write:)‾‾‾‾

B

$4 \times 2 =$ _____ $2\overline{)8}$ $3 \times 2 =$ _____ $2\overline{)6}$

$1 \times 2 =$ _____ $2\overline{)2}$ $5 \times 2 =$ _____ $2\overline{)10}$

$10 \times 2 =$ _____ $2\overline{)20}$ $9 \times 2 =$ _____ $2\overline{)18}$

$8 \times 2 =$ _____ $2\overline{)16}$ $7 \times 2 =$ _____ $2\overline{)14}$

C

THE 1-TABLE

Ask: How much is 4 times 1?   Ask: How many 1s are in 4?

Write: _____ × _____ = _____   Write:)‾‾‾‾

$1\overline{)10}^{\,10}$ $1\overline{)8}$ $1\overline{)6}$ $1\overline{)2}$ $1\overline{)9}$

$1\overline{)5}$ $1\overline{)4}$ $1\overline{)3}$ $1\overline{)1}$ $1\overline{)7}$

4

A

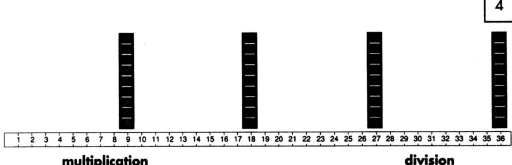

multiplication   division

Ask: How much is 4 times 9?   Ask: How many 9s are in 36?

Write: _____ × _____ = _____   Write:)‾‾‾‾‾

B

10 × 9 = _____   9)‾9̄0̄   3 × 9 = _____   9)‾2̄7̄

8 × 9 = _____   9)‾7̄2̄   4 × 9 = _____   9)‾3̄6̄

6 × 9 = _____   9)‾5̄4̄   5 × 9 = _____   9)‾4̄5̄

C Write the multiples of 9.

9									

D Divide.

9)‾4̄5̄   9)‾6̄3̄   9)‾7̄2̄   9)1̄8̄   9)‾9̄

9)‾5̄4̄   9)‾3̄6̄   9)‾8̄1̄   9)‾2̄7̄   9)‾9̄0̄

70

DIVISION: THE 9-TABLE

A

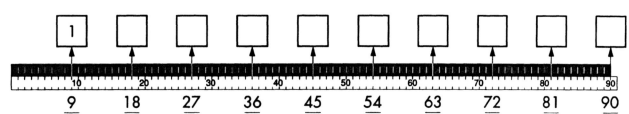

The multiples of 9 are on the lines.

In each box write how many 9s are in that multiple.

B

To check a division example, use multiplication.

To check, multiply.

$$\frac{6}{9)\overline{54}}$$

Is 6 the right answer?

$$\frac{6}{9)\overline{54}}$$

6 × 9 = 54

C

Divide. Then check each example.

$$9)\overline{36}$$ $$9)\overline{63}$$ $$9)\overline{72}$$ $$9)\overline{27}$$

check

___ × ___ = ___

check

___ × ___ = ___

check

___ × ___ = ___

check

___ × ___ = ___

D

Ms. Carr needs 9 squares of cloth to make one pillow cover. There are 72 squares in a package. How many pillow covers can she make?

Think: One pillow cover needs 9 squares.
There are 72 squares.
Ask: How many 9s in 72?

Ms. Carr can make _____ pillow covers.

71

A

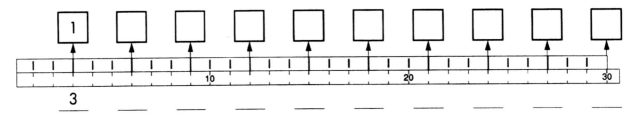

| 1 | | | | | | | | | |

3 ___ ___ ___ ___ ___ ___ ___ ___ ___

Write the multiples of 3 on the lines.
In each box write how many 3s are in that multiple.

B

To check, multiply.

How many 3s are in 18? $3\overline{)18}$ (6)   check: __6__ × 3 = __18__

How many 3s are in 12? $3\overline{)12}$ check: _____ × 3 = _____

How many 3s are in 6? $3\overline{)6}$ check: _____ × 3 = _____

C

$3\overline{)15}$ $3\overline{)9}$ $3\overline{)24}$ $3\overline{)18}$ $3\overline{)6}$

$3\overline{)30}$ $3\overline{)21}$ $3\overline{)3}$ $3\overline{)27}$ $3\overline{)12}$

D

The grade school is giving a big party for the parents. They will decorate each table with 3 candles. They bought a box of 24 candles. How many tables can they decorate with the candles in that box?
Think: Each table gets 3 candles.
Ask: How many groups of 3 in 24?

Do the example here.

They can decorate _____ tables.

Check your answer.

_____ × _____ = _____

TEST

A

Divide.

$10\overline{)20}$ $5\overline{)5}$ $9\overline{)72}$ $3\overline{)3}$ $9\overline{)9}$ $2\overline{)2}$ $1\overline{)9}$

$2\overline{)4}$ $1\overline{)10}$ $10\overline{)40}$ $5\overline{)10}$ $9\overline{)63}$ $3\overline{)6}$ $10\overline{)10}$

$2\overline{)6}$ $9\overline{)54}$ $3\overline{)9}$ $1\overline{)4}$ $10\overline{)30}$ $1\overline{)1}$ $5\overline{)15}$

$3\overline{)24}$ $10\overline{)50}$ $5\overline{)20}$ $1\overline{)2}$ $2\overline{)18}$ $9\overline{)45}$ $3\overline{)12}$

$5\overline{)25}$ $2\overline{)12}$ $9\overline{)36}$ $3\overline{)18}$ $10\overline{)60}$ $2\overline{)10}$ $5\overline{)30}$

$9\overline{)90}$ $2\overline{)14}$ $5\overline{)35}$ $10\overline{)70}$ $9\overline{)27}$ $3\overline{)21}$ $5\overline{)50}$

$2\overline{)8}$ $9\overline{)18}$ $1\overline{)3}$ $5\overline{)45}$ $10\overline{)80}$ $3\overline{)27}$ $2\overline{)16}$

$10\overline{)100}$ $1\overline{)7}$ $9\overline{)81}$ $3\overline{)30}$ $2\overline{)20}$ $10\overline{)90}$ $5\overline{)40}$

B

There are **20** chairs in the music room. The teacher asked the students to arrange them in rows of **5** chairs. How many rows will there be?

Think: One row has 5 chairs.
Ask: How many 5s in 20?

There will be _____ rows of chairs.

73

DIVISION: THE 4-TABLE

A

7

```
  1  2  3  4  5  6  7  8  9  10 11 12 13 14 15 16 17 18 19 20 21 22 23 24 25 26 27 28 29 30 31 32 33 34 35 36
```

multiplication

Ask: How much is 7 times 4?

Write: _____ × _____ = _____

division

Ask: How many 4s are in 28?

Write:) ‾‾‾‾‾‾

B

8 × 4 = _____   4)‾3̄2̄   9 × 4 = _____   4)‾3̄6̄

6 × 4 = _____   4)‾2̄4̄   7 × 4 = _____   4)‾2̄8̄

4 × 4 = _____   4)‾1̄6̄   5 × 4 = _____   4)‾2̄0̄

2 × 4 = _____   4)‾8̄   3 × 4 = _____   4)‾1̄2̄

C

Write the multiples of 4.

4									

D

8 children want to go on a boat ride. A rule says that only 4 children can ride in each boat. How many boats will they need?

Think: One boat holds 4 children.

Ask: How many groups of 4 in 8?

The teacher had 24 books. Each child took 4 books. How many children took books?

Think: One child took 4 books.

Ask: How many groups of 4 in 24?

They will need _____ boats.

_____ children took books.

74

A

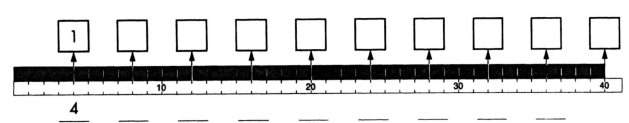

<u> 4 </u> <u>   </u> <u>   </u> <u>   </u> <u>   </u> <u>   </u> <u>   </u> <u>   </u> <u>   </u>

Write the multiples of 4 on the lines.
In each box write how many 4s are in that multiple.

B

To check, multiply.

How many 4s are in 4? $4\overline{)4}$ check: ___1___ × 4 = _____

How many 4s are in 24? $4\overline{)24}$ check: _____ × 4 = _____

How many 4s are in 32? $4\overline{)32}$ check: _____ × 4 = _____

C

Divide.

$4\overline{)32}$ $4\overline{)4}$ $4\overline{)24}$ $4\overline{)40}$ $4\overline{)20}$

$4\overline{)36}$ $4\overline{)8}$ $4\overline{)16}$ $4\overline{)28}$ $4\overline{)12}$

D

 Ken is making horses by sticking tooth-picks into potatoes. Each horse will need 4 toothpicks. If Ken has 36 toothpicks, how many horses can he make?

Think: Each horse needs 4 toothpicks.
Ask: How many groups of 4 in 36?

Ken can make _____ horses.

DIVISION: THE 6-TABLE

A

4

multiplication

Ask: How much is 4 times 6?

Write: _____ × _____ = _____

division

Ask: How many 6s are in 24?

Write:)‾‾‾‾

B

10 × 6 = _____   6)60‾‾   1 × 6 = _____   6)‾‾

8 × 6 = _____   6)48‾‾   3 × 6 = _____   6)‾‾

2 × 6 = _____   6)12‾‾   5 × 6 = _____   6)‾‾

C

Write the multiples of 6.

☐ ☐ ☐ ☐ ☐ ☐ ☐ ☐ ☐ ☐

D

The hiking club is giving a supper party. Each table seats 6 people. 24 people are coming. How many tables should the members set?
Think: 1 table seats 6 people.
Ask: How many groups of 6 are in 24?

Dad is pasting a star on each side of a cube. A cube has 6 sides. If he has 48 stars, how many cubes can he decorate?
Think: Each cube takes 6 stars.
Ask: How many 6s are in 48?

They should set _____ tables.

Dad can decorate _____ cubes.

A

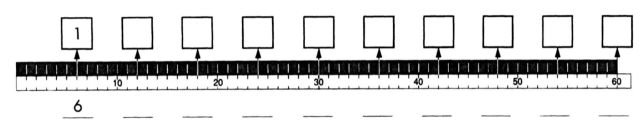

6 _____ _____ _____ _____ _____ _____ _____ _____ _____

Write the multiples of **6** on the lines.

In each box write how many 6s are in that multiple.

B

To check, multiply.

How many 6s are in 24?   6) 24   check: _____ × __6__ = _____

How many 6s are in 54?   6) 54   check: _____ × _____ = _____

How many 6s are in 42?   6) 42   check: _____ × _____ = _____

C Divide.

6) 24   6) 54   6) 12   6) 30   6) 42

6) 6   6) 48   6) 60   6) 18   6) 36

D

The children are making bran muffins for the fair. Each muffin pan makes **6** muffins. They want to make **48** muffins. How many panfuls will they need to bake?
Think: One pan makes 6 muffins.
Ask: How many 6s in 48?

They will make _____ panfuls of muffins.

77

DIVISION: THE 7-TABLE

A

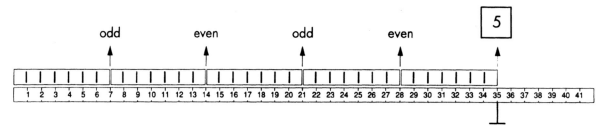

multiplication	**division**

Ask: How much is **5** times 7?   Ask: How many 7s are in **35**?

Write: _____ × _____ = _____   Write:)‾‾‾‾‾

B

10 × 7 = _____   7)‾70‾   9 × 7 = _____   7)‾63‾

8 × 7 = _____   7)‾56‾   7 × 7 = _____   7)‾49‾

6 × 7 = _____   7)‾42‾   5 × 7 = _____   7)‾35‾

4 × 7 = _____   7)‾28‾   3 × 7 = _____   7)‾21‾

2 × 7 = _____   7)‾14‾   1 × 7 = _____   7)‾7‾

C

	odd	even	odd	even	odd	even	odd	even	odd	even
Write the multiples of 7.										

D

There are **28** days in February.
Finish writing in the days.

1	2	3	4	5	6	7
8						

How many weeks are in **28** days?
Ask: How many 7s in **28**?

There are _____ weeks in **28** days.

A

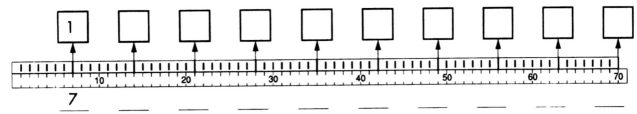

7 ___ ___ ___ ___ ___ ___ ___ --- ___

Write the multiples of 7 on the lines.

In each box write how many 7s are in that multiple.

B

To check, multiply.

How many 7s are in 14?   7)14   check: _____ × _____ = _____

How many 7s are in 63?   7)   check: _____ × _____ = _____

How many 7s are in 49?   7)   check: _____ × _____ = _____

C   Divide.

7)35   7)14   7)42   7)7   7)63

7)28   7)56   7)21   7)70   7)49

D

The teacher said, "There are 21 days until vacation." The children want to know how many weeks that is.

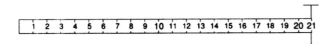

Think: One week has 7 days.
Ask: How many 7s are in 21?

The children found that 21 days equal _____ weeks.

79

A

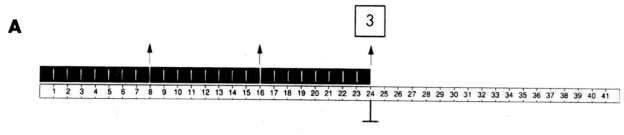

multiplication

Ask: How much is 3 times 8?

Write: _____ × _____ = _____

division

Ask: How many 8s are in 24?

Write:)‾‾‾‾‾

B

8 × 8 = _____   8)‾64‾

6 × 8 = _____   8)‾48‾

4 × 8 = _____   8)‾32‾

7 × 8 = _____   8)‾56‾

5 × 8 = _____   8)‾40‾

9 × 8 = _____   8)‾72‾

C

Write the multiples of 8.

☐ ☐ ☐ ☐ ☐ ☐ ☐ ☐ ☐ ☐

D

There are **24** chairs in the computer room. Ms. Guzman asked Joseph to arrange them in rows of **8**. How many rows can he make?
Think: One row has 8 chairs.
Ask: How many 8s in 24?

Mr. Barron needs **32** pencils for his class of children. Pencils come **8** to a box. How many boxes of pencils must he buy?
Think: One box has 8 pencils.
Ask: How many 8s in 32?

Joseph can make _____ rows of chairs.

Mr. Barron must buy _____ boxes.

DIVISION: THE 8-TABLE

A

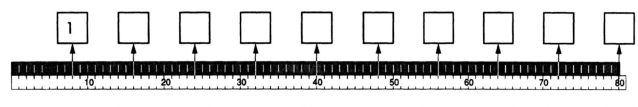

Write the multiples of 8 on the lines.

In each box write how many 8s are in that multiple.

B

To check, multiply.

How many 8s are in 16?   8)‾1‾6‾   check: _____ × _____ = _____

How many 8s are in 48?   8)‾4‾8‾   check: _____ × _____ = _____

How many 8s are in 32?   8)‾3‾2‾   check: _____ × _____ = _____

C Divide.

8)‾6‾4‾   8)‾7‾2‾   8)‾8‾0‾   8)‾5‾6‾   8)‾4‾0‾

8)‾8‾   8)‾2‾4‾   8)‾3‾2‾   8)‾1‾6‾   8)‾4‾8‾

D

The farmer wants to pack 8 apples into each box. There are 48 apples. How many boxes can the farmer pack with apples?
Think: One box holds _____ apples.
Ask: How many 8s in 48?

The teacher has a box of 80 sheets of paper. Each child is going to make a book with 10 sheets. How many children can make books from 80 sheets of paper?
Think: One child needs _____ sheets.
Ask: How many 10s in 80?

The farmer can pack _____ boxes with apples.

_____ children can make books.

A

The principal has $50 to give as prizes. If each prize is $5, how many prizes can she give?
We know the total amount.
We know the size of each share.
We want to know how many shares.
Ask: How many 5s in 50?

$$5\overline{)\,50}$$

She can give _____ prizes.

The principal has $50 to give as prizes to 10 children. How much will each prize be?
We know the total amount.
We know how many shares.
We want to know the size of each share.
Ask: 50 divided by 10 is how much?

We can write $50 \div 10 =$ _____

or we can write $10\overline{)\,50}$.

Each prize will be $_____.

B

Ann's grandmother saved 24 dolls from her childhood. She wants to divide them equally among her 3 grandchildren. How many dolls will each child get?
Think: 24 divided by 3

_____ ÷ _____ = _____

Jan cooked 8 hamburgers. There were 4 children at the cookout. If Jan divides the hamburgers equally among the children, what will the share of each child be?
Think: 8 divided by 4

_____ ÷ _____ = _____

Each child will get _____ dolls.

Each child will get _____ hamburgers.

C

27 ÷ 3 = _____	27 ÷ 9 = _____	14 ÷ 2 = _____	63 ÷ 7 = _____
56 ÷ 8 = _____	42 ÷ 6 = _____	72 ÷ 8 = _____	36 ÷ 6 = _____
63 ÷ 9 = _____	35 ÷ 7 = _____	24 ÷ 3 = _____	81 ÷ 9 = _____
42 ÷ 7 = _____	18 ÷ 3 = _____	48 ÷ 6 = _____	48 ÷ 8 = _____
54 ÷ 6 = _____	64 ÷ 8 = _____	72 ÷ 9 = _____	12 ÷ 4 = _____
35 ÷ 5 = _____	28 ÷ 4 = _____	15 ÷ 5 = _____	21 ÷ 3 = _____

A

Divide.

$24 \div 4 =$ _____ $54 \div 9 =$ _____ $45 \div 9 =$ _____ $40 \div 8 =$ _____

$18 \div 6 =$ _____ $32 \div 8 =$ _____ $32 \div 4 =$ _____ $28 \div 7 =$ _____

$56 \div 7 =$ _____ $21 \div 7 =$ _____ $49 \div 7 =$ _____ $36 \div 4 =$ _____

B

My cousin bought 20 packages of base-ball cards for the party. If 10 children come to the party, how many packages will each child get?
Ask: 20 divided by 10 is how many?

Each child will get _____ packages.

Matthew has 12 toy cars. He wants his 2 friends and himself to have the same number. How many will each get?
Ask: 12 divided by 3 is how many?

Each child will get _____ cars.

There are 24 children in first grade. 6 parents brought their cars to drive them to a picnic. The same number of children will ride in each car. How many children will ride in each car?

_____ children will ride in each car.

The 4 grandchildren cleaned their grandfather's garage. He gave them $20 to share equally. How much did each child get?

Each child got $_____.

Kumi bought a bag of 48 marbles. She wanted to divide them equally among the 8 children at the birthday party. How many will each child get?

Each child will get _____ marbles.

3 children are making valentines. There are 24 sheets of red paper. Each child wants an equal share. How many sheets of paper will each child get?

Each child will get _____ sheets.

A

Divide.

$2\overline{)12}$ $8\overline{)64}$ $4\overline{)24}$ $1\overline{)1}$ $3\overline{)3}$ $5\overline{)20}$ $6\overline{)12}$

$6\overline{)60}$ $9\overline{)63}$ $3\overline{)6}$ $7\overline{)56}$ $9\overline{)72}$ $2\overline{)18}$ $6\overline{)42}$

$7\overline{)7}$ $9\overline{)36}$ $2\overline{)4}$ $5\overline{)10}$ $8\overline{)8}$ $1\overline{)9}$ $3\overline{)27}$

$2\overline{)20}$ $9\overline{)54}$ $4\overline{)4}$ $2\overline{)6}$ $9\overline{)27}$ $4\overline{)36}$ $8\overline{)40}$

$1\overline{)3}$ $6\overline{)24}$ $4\overline{)16}$ $10\overline{)80}$ $4\overline{)8}$ $7\overline{)21}$ $1\overline{)7}$

$8\overline{)48}$ $1\overline{)10}$ $10\overline{)100}$ $5\overline{)25}$ $7\overline{)49}$ $1\overline{)6}$ $8\overline{)80}$

B

$72 \div 8 =$ _____ $21 \div 3 =$ _____ $32 \div 4 =$ _____ $48 \div 6 =$ _____

$15 \div 5 =$ _____ $35 \div 7 =$ _____ $14 \div 7 =$ _____ $15 \div 3 =$ _____

C

The teacher wants to move **42** books to the library. If each child carries **6** books, how many children will the teacher need to carry books?

Ask: How many groups of _____ are in _____?

The principal had **20** goldfish to give to third graders. If **10** children want goldfish, how many will each child get?

Think: 20 divided by 10.

The teacher will need _____ children.

Each child will get _____ goldfish.

A

Divide.

$$6\overline{)30} \qquad 8\overline{)24} \qquad 4\overline{)20} \qquad 5\overline{)30} \qquad 8\overline{)64} \qquad 7\overline{)56} \qquad 6\overline{)42}$$

$$9\overline{)9} \qquad 2\overline{)16} \qquad 10\overline{)60} \qquad 10\overline{)40} \qquad 3\overline{)30} \qquad 3\overline{)12} \qquad 1\overline{)4}$$

$$1\overline{)8} \qquad 10\overline{)90} \qquad 6\overline{)54} \qquad 3\overline{)18} \qquad 8\overline{)48} \qquad 6\overline{)18} \qquad 4\overline{)12}$$

$$5\overline{)40} \qquad 6\overline{)36} \qquad 3\overline{)24} \qquad 2\overline{)10} \qquad 2\overline{)8} \qquad 8\overline{)16} \qquad 5\overline{)35}$$

$$10\overline{)20} \qquad 9\overline{)81} \qquad 4\overline{)40} \qquad 9\overline{)45} \qquad 1\overline{)5} \qquad 8\overline{)32} \qquad 4\overline{)28}$$

$$7\overline{)63} \qquad 9\overline{)18} \qquad 5\overline{)5} \qquad 7\overline{)14} \qquad 7\overline{)28} \qquad 3\overline{)9} \qquad 7\overline{)49}$$

B

$42 \div 7 = $ _____ $70 \div 10 = $ _____ $56 \div 8 = $ _____ $36 \div 6 = $ _____

$2 \div 2 = $ _____ $64 \div 8 = $ _____ $28 \div 7 = $ _____ $80 \div 10 = $ _____

C

The lunchroom is getting new tables. Each table needs 4 legs. If you saw a pile of 36 legs, how many new tables would you think there will be?

Ask: How many _____ in _____?

Mr. Brown has 4 pots to plant bulbs in. He bought a package of 20 bulbs. He wants to plant the same number in each pot. How many bulbs will he plant in each pot?

Think: 20 divided by 4.

There will be _____ new tables.

He will plant _____ bulbs in each pot.

A

$$\overset{?}{5) \overline{23}}$$ How many 5s are in 23?

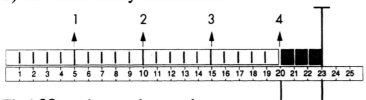

Find **23** on the number track.

How many 5s fit into 23? _____ of the 5-blocks.

4 of the 5 blocks reach only to **20**. What is the difference between **20** and **23**?

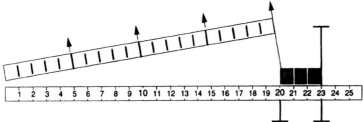

Subtract **20** from **23** to find what is left.

3 cubes are left. They remain in the track.

We call **3** the **remainder**.

B

How to write the example:

$$\overset{?}{5) \overline{23}} \qquad \overset{\nearrow 4}{5) \overline{23}} \qquad \overset{4 \; R \; \_\_}{5) \overline{23}}$$
$$\phantom{5) \overline{23}} \qquad \underline{} \qquad -20$$
$$\phantom{5) \overline{23} xxxxx} \underline{}$$

Ask: How many 5s are in 23?
Think: What is the next lower multiple of 5? It is 20.
How many 5s are in 20? _____

Write 4 as the answer.
Multiply 4 × 5 = 20.
Write 20 below 23.

Next, subtract 20 from 23.
Write 3 under 20, and write 3 again in the quotient after R.

C Divide.

$$5) \overline{7}^{\;\_\_ R \_\_} \qquad 5) \overline{31}^{\;\_\_ R \_\_} \qquad 5) \overline{44}^{\;\_\_ R \_\_} \qquad 5) \overline{16}^{\;\_\_ R \_\_} \qquad 5) \overline{29}^{\;\_\_ R \_\_}$$

A

$$3\overline{)17}^{\;?}$$ How many 3s are in 17?

Find 17 on the number track.

How many 3s fit into 17? _____ of the 3-blocks.

But 5 of the 3-blocks reach only to 15. What is the difference between 15 and 17?

Subtract 15 from 17 to find what is left.

2 cubes are left. They remain in the track. We call 2 the remainder.

B

How to write the example:

$$3\overline{)17}^{\;?}$$

$$3\overline{)17}^{\;\;5}$$
_____

$$3\overline{)17}^{\;\;5\;R\_}$$
$$-15$$
___

Ask: How many 3s are in 17?
Think: What is the next lower
multiple of 3? It is _____.
How many 3s are in 15? _____

Write 5 as the answer.
Multiply 5 × 3 = 15.
Write 15 below 17.

Next, subtract 15 from 17.
Write 2 under 15, and
write 2 again in the quotient
after R.

C

$$3\overline{)4}^{\;\_R\_}$$ $$3\overline{)16}^{\;\_R\_}$$ $$3\overline{)19}^{\;\_R\_}$$ $$3\overline{)23}^{\;\_R\_}$$ $$3\overline{)10}^{\;\_R\_}$$

$$3\overline{)11}^{\;\_R\_}$$ $$3\overline{)13}^{\;\_R\_}$$ $$3\overline{)26}^{\;\_R\_}$$ $$3\overline{)28}^{\;\_R\_}$$ $$3\overline{)7}^{\;\_R\_}$$

87

A

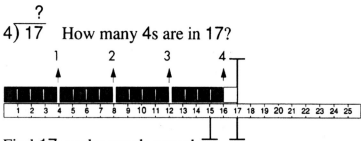

$$4\overline{)17}^{\,?}$$ How many 4s are in 17?

Find 17 on the number track.

How many 4s fit into 17? _____ of the 4-blocks.

4 of the 4-blocks reach only to 16. What is the difference between 16 and 17? _____

B

How to write the example:

$$4\overline{)17}^{\,?}$$ $$4\overline{)17}$$ _____ $$4\overline{)17}^{\,=\,R\,\_}$$ $$-\,\_\_$$ $$\_$$

Ask: How many 4s are in 17? Think: What is the next lower multiple of 4? It is _____. How many 4s are in 16? _____

Write 4 as the answer. Multiply 4 × 4 = 16. Write 16 below 17.

Next, subtract 16 from 17. Write 1 under 16, and write 1 again in the quotient after R.

C

Write the multiples of 4.

D

$$4\overline{)33}^{\,=\,R\,\_}$$ $$4\overline{)39}^{\,=\,R\,\_}$$ $$4\overline{)19}^{\,=\,R\,\_}$$ $$4\overline{)22}^{\,=\,R\,\_}$$ $$4\overline{)10}^{\,=\,R\,\_}$$

$$4\overline{)11}^{\,=\,R\,\_}$$ $$4\overline{)13}^{\,=\,R\,\_}$$ $$4\overline{)26}^{\,=\,R\,\_}$$ $$4\overline{)31}^{\,=\,R\,\_}$$ $$4\overline{)5}^{\,=\,R\,\_}$$

A

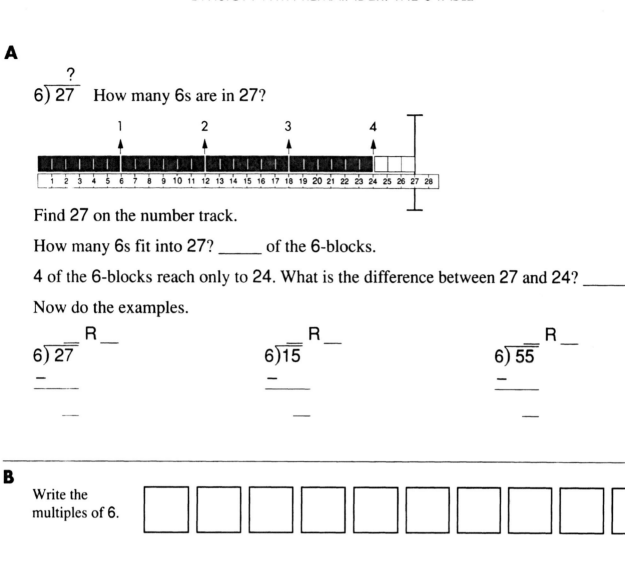

6) 27   How many 6s are in 27?

Find 27 on the number track.

How many 6s fit into 27? _____ of the 6-blocks.

4 of the 6-blocks reach only to 24. What is the difference between 27 and 24? _____

Now do the examples.

6) 27   R __

6)15   R __

6) 55   R __

B

Write the
multiples of 6.

☐ ☐ ☐ ☐ ☐ ☐ ☐ ☐ ☐ ☐

C

6) 34   R __

6) 26   R __

6) 23   R __

6)19   R __

6)11   R __

6) 40   R __

6) 51   R __

6) 46   R __

A

The short form

$\overset{?}{2)17}$ How many 2s are in 17?

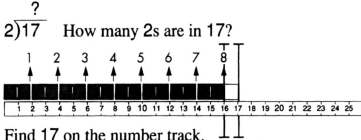

Find 17 on the number track.

In the short form you do the work in your head.

Think: The next lower multiple of 2 is 16.

How many times does 2 go into 16? _____ times.

Write 8 as the answer to the example.

Think: 17 − 16 = 1. This is the remainder.

Write 1 after R in the quotient.

$2)\overline{17}$ R __

B

Divide using the short form.

$2)\overline{5}$ R __ $2)\overline{15}$ R __ $2)\overline{19}$ R __ $2)\overline{13}$ R __

$2)\overline{11}$ R __ $2)\overline{9}$ R __ $2)\overline{17}$ R __ $2)\overline{7}$ R __

$3)\overline{7}$ R __ $4)\overline{10}$ R __ $5)\overline{13}$ R __ $6)\overline{11}$ R __

$5)\overline{36}$ R __ $3)\overline{17}$ R __ $6)\overline{35}$ R __ $4)\overline{23}$ R __

$6)\overline{39}$ R __ $4)\overline{15}$ R __ $3)\overline{10}$ R __ $5)\overline{23}$ R __

A

$$\overset{?}{10)\overline{35}}$$ How many 10s are in 35?

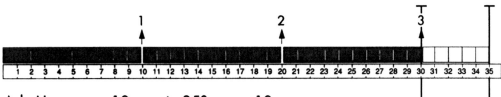

Ask: How many 10s are in 35? _____ 10s.
3 of the 10-blocks reach only to 30.
30 is the next lower multiple of 10.
How many times does 10 go into 30? _____ times.
To get the remainder, subtract 35 − 30 = 5.

B

Do the example.

$$10)\overline{35}^{\underline{\underline{}}R\_} \longleftarrow \text{dividend}$$

To check the answer:
Multiply.   3 × 10 =   30
Add the remainder.   + 5

This number should be the   35
same as the dividend.

C

Divide and check.

$$10)\overline{85}^{\underline{\underline{}}R\_} \qquad 10)\overline{22}^{\underline{\underline{}}R\_} \qquad 10)\overline{67}^{\underline{\underline{}}R\_} \qquad 10)\overline{48}^{\underline{\underline{}}R\_}$$

To check:
Multiply.
Add the remainder.
Is the number the same?

$$10)\overline{14}^{\underline{\underline{}}R\_} \qquad 10)\overline{39}^{\underline{\underline{}}R\_} \qquad 10)\overline{76}^{\underline{\underline{}}R\_} \qquad 10)\overline{53}^{\underline{\underline{}}R\_}$$

To check:
Multiply.
Add the remainder.
Is the number the same?

A

$$7\overline{)41}^{\,?}$$

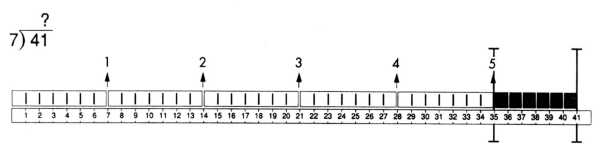

Find 41 on the number track.

How many 7s are in 41?

The next lower multiple of 7 is _____.

Do the example.

$$7\overline{)41}^{\quad = \;R\;\_\_}$$
$$\underline{-}$$
$$\overline{}$$

B

Write the multiples of 7.

C

Divide.

$$7\overline{)39}^{\;=\;R\;\_}\qquad 7\overline{)20}^{\;=\;R\;\_}\qquad 7\overline{)54}^{\;=\;R\;\_}\qquad 7\overline{)69}^{\;=\;R\;\_}$$

To check:
Multiply.
Add the remainder.
Is the number the same?

Solve by short division.

$$7\overline{)43}^{\;=\;R\;\_}\qquad 7\overline{)23}^{\;=\;R\;\_}\qquad 7\overline{)62}^{\;=\;R\;\_}\qquad 7\overline{)50}^{\;=\;R\;\_}$$

A

$$8\overline{)39}^{\,?}$$

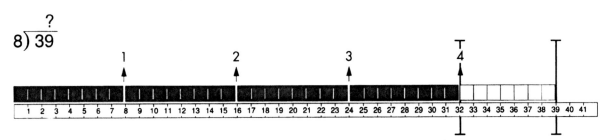

Find 39 on the number track.

How many 8s are in 39?

The next lower multiple of 8 is _____.

Do the example.

$$8\overline{)39}^{\,\_\ R\ \_}$$

B

Write the
multiples of 8.

C

Divide and check.

$8\overline{)25}^{\,\_\ R\ \_}$ $8\overline{)13}^{\,\_\ R\ \_}$ $8\overline{)31}^{\,\_\ R\ \_}$ $8\overline{)50}^{\,\_\ R\ \_}$ $8\overline{)35}^{\,\_\ R\ \_}$

$8\overline{)49}^{\,\_\ R\ \_}$ $8\overline{)22}^{\,\_\ R\ \_}$ $8\overline{)61}^{\,\_\ R\ \_}$ $8\overline{)76}^{\,\_\ R\ \_}$ $8\overline{)65}^{\,\_\ R\ \_}$

A

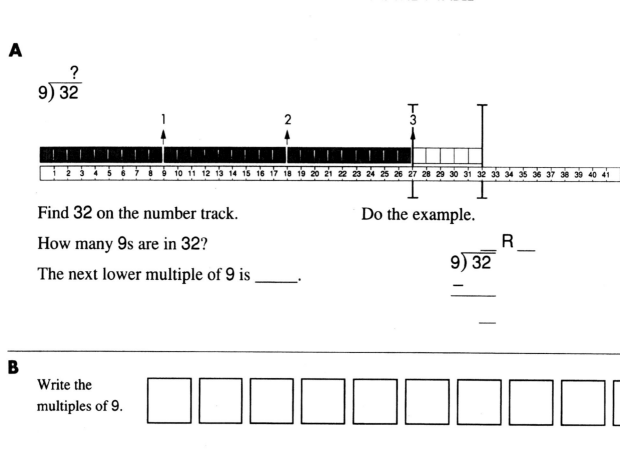

$$9\overline{)32}^{?}$$

Find **32** on the number track.

How many 9s are in 32?

The next lower multiple of 9 is _____.

Do the example.

$$9\overline{)32}\,\text{R}\,\_$$
$$\_$$
$$\_$$

B

Write the
multiples of 9.

C Divide and check.

$$9\overline{)57}\,\text{R}\,\_\quad 9\overline{)11}\,\text{R}\,\_\quad 9\overline{)88}\,\text{R}\,\_\quad 9\overline{)60}\,\text{R}\,\_\quad 9\overline{)41}\,\text{R}\,\_$$

$$9\overline{)26}\,\text{R}\,\_\quad 9\overline{)49}\,\text{R}\,\_\quad 9\overline{)19}\,\text{R}\,\_\quad 9\overline{)75}\,\text{R}\,\_\quad 9\overline{)71}\,\text{R}\,\_$$

94

A

Study of remainders

The 2-table   The remainder is always ____.

The 3-table   The remainder could be ____ or ____.

The 4-table   The remainder could be ____, ____, or ____.

The 5-table  The remainder could be ____, ____, ____, ____.

The 6-table The remainder could be ____, ____, ____,
____, or ____.

B

Solve by long division.

5)12 R __   6)39 R __   3)20 R __   8)54 R __   7)69 R __

2)13 R __   5)23 R __   7)39 R __   7)62 R __   7)50 R __

10)78 R __   9)64 R __   6)57 R __   3)26 R __   4)39 R __

C

Solve by short division.

8)63 R __   10)91 R __   4)31 R __   2)19 R __   9)89 R __

A

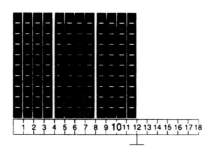

Stand 3 times 4 tens in the track.

3 × **4** tens = **12** tens

3 × **40** = **120**

$$\begin{array}{r} \mathbf{40} \\ \times\ \mathbf{3} \\ \hline \mathbf{120} \end{array}$$ = 120

B

40	70	20	80	60	50
× 3	× 4	× 9	× 3	× 2	× 3

30	20	50	90	40	30
× 7	× 8	× 6	× 2	× 4	× 6

C

Carlos weighs 50 pounds. His father weighs 3 times as much. How much does his father weigh?

Pencils cost 30¢ each. Jackie wants to buy 3 pencils. How much will they cost?

His father weighs _____ pounds.

3 pencils will cost _____¢.

96

A

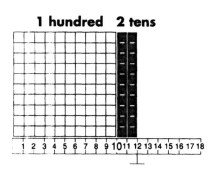

Here is one hundred twenty.

How many groups of 40 are in 120?

$$40\overline{)120}$$

Think:
40 does not go into 12.
40 does go into 120.
Make a line over 0 for your
answer.

$$40\overline{)120}$$

Think:
40 goes into 120
3 times.
Write 3 on the line
in the answer.

$$\begin{array}{r} 3 \\ 40\overline{)120} \\ -\quad 0 \end{array}$$

Multiply 3 × 0 = 0.
Write 0 below 0.
3 × 4 tens is 12 tens.
Write 12 below 12.
120 − 120 = 0.

B

$$40\overline{)120}$$
$$-\rule{2cm}{0.4pt}$$

$$20\overline{)180}$$
$$-\rule{2cm}{0.4pt}$$

$$30\overline{)210}$$
$$-\rule{2cm}{0.4pt}$$

$$40\overline{)320}$$
$$-\rule{2cm}{0.4pt}$$

$$70\overline{)280}$$
$$-\rule{2cm}{0.4pt}$$

$$30\overline{)180}$$
$$-\rule{2cm}{0.4pt}$$

$$20\overline{)120}$$
$$-\rule{2cm}{0.4pt}$$

$$80\overline{)640}$$
$$-\rule{2cm}{0.4pt}$$

MULTIPLICATION AND DIVISION

A

	90	80	60	70	50	40
	× 3	× 4	× 6	× 7	× 9	× 8

	40	70	60	80	90	20
	× 3	× 4	× 5	× 6	× 7	× 8

B

60)240   20)180   10)60   40)280   30)270

40)80   50)150   30)120   60)540   20)160

C

Oranges are 30¢ apiece. If mother spent 90¢, how many oranges did she buy?

Pears are 20¢ each. Mrs. Box bought 4 pears. How much did she pay?

Mother bought _____ oranges.

Mrs. Box paid _____¢.

Grapefruits are 40¢ apiece. The children spent 80¢. How many grapefruits did they buy?

Lemons are 20¢ each. What will 3 lemons cost?

The children bought _____ grapefruits.

3 lemons will cost _____¢.

98

A

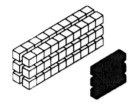

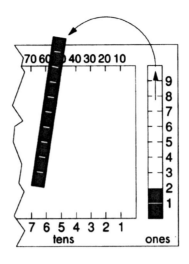

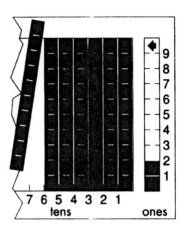

```
  24
×  3
```

```
 1
 2 4
×   3
─────
     2
```

```
 1
 2 4
×   3
─────
 7 2
```

Look at the blocks.
You see 3 times 24.

First multiply the ones:
$3 \times 4 = 12$.
Write 2 in the ones place.
Carry 1 ten to the tens place.

Next multiply the tens:
3×2 tens $= 6$ tens.
6 tens + 1 ten $= 7$ tens.
Write 7 in the tens place.

B

24	25	48	12	15	21
× 3	× 3	× 2	× 5	× 6	× 4
18	26	26	24	15	49
× 5	× 2	× 3	× 4	× 5	× 2

MULTIPLYING TWO-PLACE NUMBERS

A

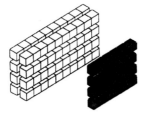

4 times 26

$$\begin{array}{r} 26 \\ \times\ 4 \\ \hline \end{array}$$

B

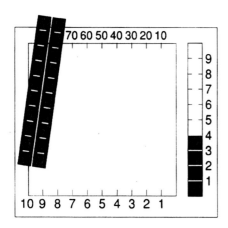

$$\begin{array}{r} \overset{2}{2}6 \\ \times\ 4 \\ \hline 4 \end{array}$$

First multiply the ones:
4 × 6 = 24.
Write 4 in the ones place.
Carry the 2 tens to the tens column.

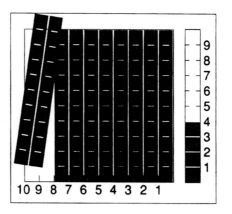

$$\begin{array}{r} \overset{2}{2}6 \\ \times\ 4 \\ \hline 1\ 0\ 4 \end{array}$$

Next multiply the tens:
4 × 2 tens = 8 tens.
8 tens + 2 tens = 10 tens.
Write 10 in the answer.
We have 10 tens and 4 ones.
We call 104 "one hundred four."

C

26	35	45	58	62	76
× 4	× 5	× 3	× 2	× 6	× 5

42	52	92	64	38	55
× 7	× 8	× 9	× 4	× 3	× 5

100

A

Multiply.

23	32	45	54	66	77
× 6	× 7	× 8	× 9	× 5	× 4

65	54	83	74	38	85
× 8	× 9	× 7	× 6	× 4	× 3

B

Divide.

20)80   50)100   30)150   60)240   20)120

_____   _____   _____   _____   _____

C

Jack wrote 3 letters. Each stamp costs 29¢. How much will 3 stamps cost?

Mrs. Kim needs 4 books for her class. Each book costs $22. How much will she spend in all?

3 stamps will cost _____¢.

She will spend $_____.

Jon is 14 years old. His mother is 4 times as old as he is. How old is his mother?

Anthony makes $45 each week by cutting grass. How much will he make in 4 weeks?

His mother is _____ years old.

Anthony will make $_____.

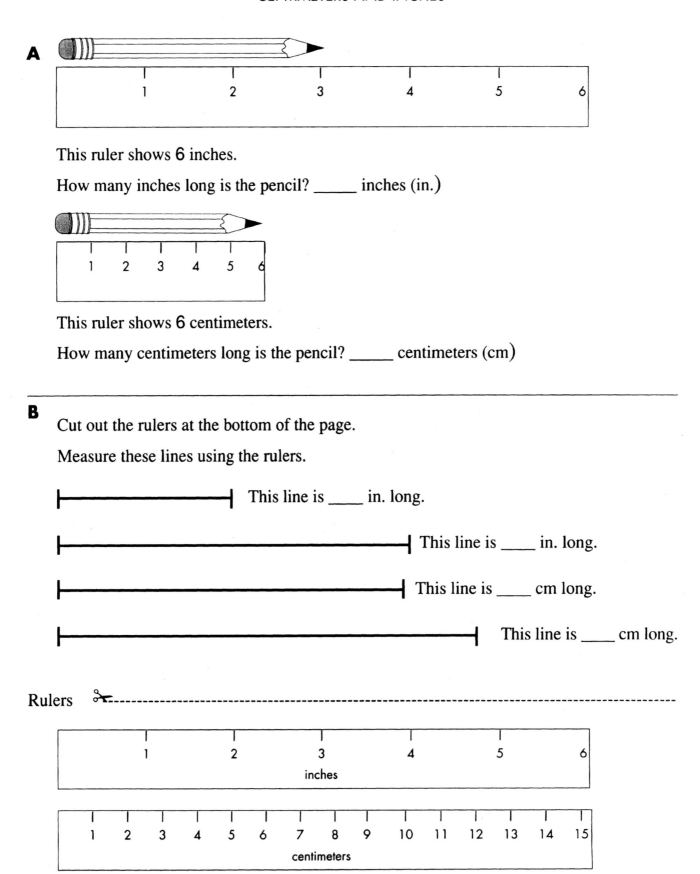

A

This ruler shows **6** inches.

How many inches long is the pencil? _____ inches (in.)

This ruler shows **6** centimeters.

How many centimeters long is the pencil? _____ centimeters (cm)

B Cut out the rulers at the bottom of the page.

Measure these lines using the rulers.

This line is ____ in. long.

This line is ____ in. long.

This line is ____ cm long.

This line is ____ cm long.

Rulers

inches

centimeters

METERS AND CENTIMETERS

The length of each strip is 10 cm. If you put 10 strips end to end, they measure 1 meter (m) .

100 cm = 1 m

200 cm = _____ m

300 cm = _____ m

600 cm = _____ m

Draw a line that is 7 cm long above the first strip.

1 m = _____ cm

2 m = _____ cm

5 m = _____ cm

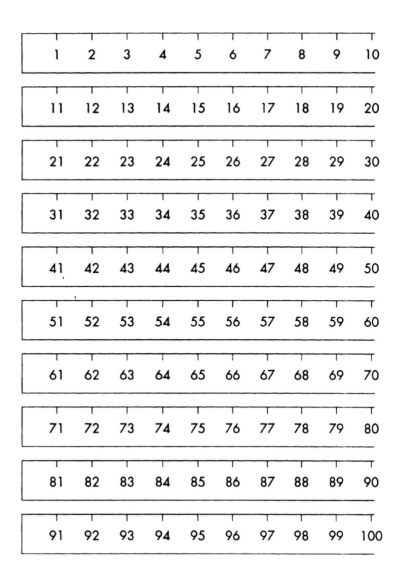

Look at the strips above.

Draw a line around the right answer and fill in the blank.

The door knob is about __1__ meter from the floor.   ①   6   10

This page is a little more than _____ centimeters wide.   3   20   80

Your hand is about _____ centimeters long.   5   60   12

Your desk is about _____ centimeters wide.   60   120   10

The ceiling in the classroom is about _____ meters high.   1   4   50

A traffic light could be _____ meters high.   100   5   300

A

Changing dimes to cents

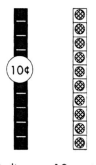

1 dime = 10 cents

 =

10 is the key number in problems about dimes and cents.

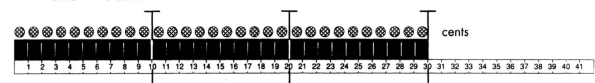

cents

How many cents are in 3 dimes?

Think: 1 dime = _____ cents.

3 dimes = __3__ × __10__ cents,

so 3 dimes = _____ cents.

8 dimes = _____ × _____ cents,

so 8 dimes = _____ cents.

6 dimes = _____ × _____ cents,

so 6 dimes = _____ cents.

B

Changing cents to dimes

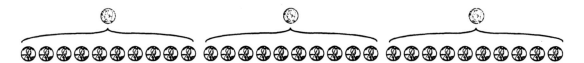

How many groups of 10 are in 30?

10) 30‾

Since you can divide by 10 in your head, you can write the answer immediately.

50¢ = _____ dimes

30¢ = _____ dimes

40¢ = _____ dimes

90¢ = _____ dimes

70¢ = _____ dimes

A

Changing nickels to cents

 =   =

1 nickel = 5 cents

2 nickels = 2 × 5 cents
2 nickels = 10 cents

5 is the key number in problems about nickels and cents.

3 nickels = _____ cents

Think: 1 nickel = _____ cents.

3 nickels = __3__ × __5__ cents,

so 3 nickels = _____ cents.

9 nickels = ____ × ____ = ____ cents

7 nickels = ____ × ____ = ____ cents

5 nickels = ____ × ____ = ____ cents

B

Changing cents to nickels

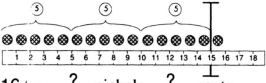

16¢ = __?__ nickels __?__ cents

Think: How many 5s are in 16?   5)‾16‾ = __ R __

16¢ = _____ nickels _____ cent

Cents	How many 5s?	Nickels and cents
18¢	5)‾18‾ = __ R __	18¢ = _____ nickels _____ cents
34¢	5)‾‾‾ = __ R __	34¢ = _____ nickels _____ cents
27¢	5)‾‾‾ = __ R __	27¢ = _____ nickels _____ cents

105

A

Changing yards to feet

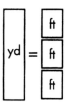 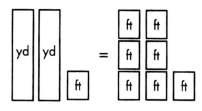

> 3 is the key number in problems about yards (yd) and feet (ft).

1 yd = 3 ft   2 yd 1 ft = 2 × 3 + 1 = 7 ft

4 yards = ___?___ feet   4 yards 1 foot = ___?___ feet

4 yd = __4__ × __3__ = ____ ft   4 yd 1 ft = ____ × ____ + ____ = ____ ft

10 yd = ____ × ____ = ____ ft   10 yd 2 ft = ____ × ____ + ____ = ____ ft

5 yd = ____ × ____ = ____ ft   5 yd 1 ft = ____ × ____ + ____ = ____ ft

---

B

Changing feet to yards

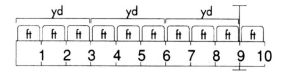

These 10 feet have been divided into groups of 3, and we have a remainder of 1 foot.

10 ft = ___?___ yd ___?___ ft

Think: How many 3s are in 10? $\overset{=\quad R\,\_}{3)\overline{10}}$

10 ft = _____ yd _____ ft

Feet	How many 3s?	Yards and feet
13 ft	$\overset{==\quad R\,\_}{3)\overline{13}}$	13 ft = _____ yd _____ ft
24 ft	$3)\overline{}$	24 ft = _____ yd _____ ft
4 ft	$\overset{=\quad R\,\_}{3)\overline{}}$	4 ft = _____ yd _____ ft

106

A

Changing feet to inches

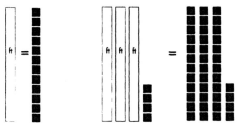

1 ft = 12 in.   3 ft 4 in. = 3 × 12 + 4 = 40 in.

12 is the key number in problems about feet and inches.

3 feet = __?__ inches

3 ft = __3__ × __12__ = ____ in.   2 ft 6 in. = ___ × ___ + ___ = ____ in.

4 ft = ___ × 12 = ____ in.   3 ft 2 in. = ___ × ___ + ___ = ____ in.

2 ft = ___ × 12 = ____ in.   2 ft 10 in. = ___ × ___ + ___ = ____ in.

B

Changing inches to feet

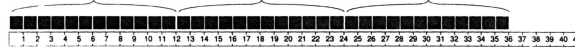

36 inches = __?__ feet

These 36 inches have been divided into groups of 12.

Think: How many 12s in 36?   12) 36‾‾

36 inches = _____ feet

Inches	How many 12s?	Feet and inches
18 in.	12) 18‾‾ R __	18 in. = _____ ft _____ in.
30 in.	12) 30‾‾ R __	30 in. = _____ ft _____ in.
40 in.	12) 40‾‾ R __	40 in. = _____ ft _____ in.

107

A Changing quarts to cups

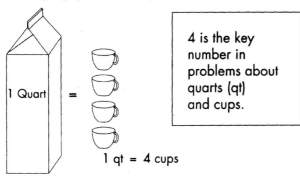

4 is the key number in problems about quarts (qt) and cups.

1 qt = 4 cups

3 quarts = ___?___ cups

3 qt = 3 × 4 = _____ cups

6 qt = 6 × _____ = _____ cups

5 qt = 5 × _____ = _____ cups

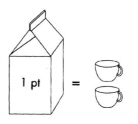

2 is the key number in problems about pints (pt) and cups.

1 pt = 2 cups

3 pints = ___?___ cups

3 pt = 3 × 2 = _____ cups

6 pt = _____ × _____ = _____ cups

4 pt = _____ × _____ = _____ cups

B Changing cups to quarts

| 1 | 2 | 3 | 4 | 5 | 6 | 7 | 8 | 9 | 10 |

How many groups of 4 are in 9?

9 cups = ___?___ quarts ___?___ cups

Think: How many 4s are in 9? $4\overline{)9}$ = ___ R ___

9 cups = _____ qt _____ cup

Cups	How many 4s?	Quarts and cups
13 cups	$4\overline{)13}$ = ___ R ___	13 cups = _____ qt _____ cup
20 cups	$4\overline{)}$ =	20 cups = _____ qt _____ cups
7 cups	$4\overline{)}$ = ___ R ___	7 cups = _____ qt _____ cups

A Changing gallons to quarts

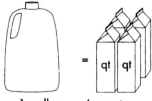

1 gallon = 4 quarts

4 is the key number
in problems about
gallons (gal) and quarts.

3 gallons = ___?___ quarts

3 gal = 3 × 4 = 12 qt

4 gal = ___ × ___ = ___ qt   4 gal 1 qt = _4_ × _4_ + _1_ = ___ qt

6 gal = ___ × ___ = ___ qt   6 gal 3 qt = ___ × ___ + ___ = ___ qt

2 gal = ___ × ___ = ___ qt   5 gal 2 qt = ___ × ___ + ___ = ___ qt

B Changing quarts to gallons

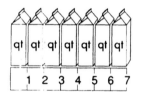

How many groups of 4 are in 7?

7 quarts = ___?___ gallons ___?___ quarts

Think: How many 4s are in 7?   4)‾7‾ R __

7 qt = _____ gal _____ qt

Quarts	How many 4s?	Gallons and quarts
14 qt	4)‾1‾4 R __	14 qt = _____ gal _____ qt
16 qt	4)‾1‾6	16 qt = _____ gal _____ qt
21 qt	4)‾_ R __	21 qt = _____ gal _____ qt

A

Changing weeks to days

One Week						
Sun	Mon	Tues	Wed	Th	Fri	Sat

1 week = 7 days

This is 1 month

1	2	3	4	5	6	7
8	9	10	11	12	13	14
15	16	17	18	19	20	21
22	23	24	25	26	27	28

4 weeks = 28 days
4 weeks = 1 month

7 is the key number in problems about weeks (wk) and days.

3 weeks = $\underline{\ ?\ }$ days

3 weeks = $\underline{\ 3\ } \times \underline{\ 7\ } = \underline{\ 21\ }$ days

2 wk = $\underline{\ 2\ } \times \underline{\quad} = \underline{\quad}$ days   2 wk 1 day = $\underline{\quad} \times \underline{\quad} + 1 = \underline{\quad}$ days

6 wk = $\underline{\quad} \times \underline{\quad} = \underline{\quad}$ days   4 wk 2 days = $\underline{\quad} \times \underline{\quad} + 2 = \underline{\quad}$ days

8 wk = $\underline{\quad} \times \underline{\quad} = \underline{\quad}$ days   3 wk 4 days = $\underline{\quad} \times \underline{\quad} + 4 = \underline{\quad}$ days

---

B

Changing days to weeks

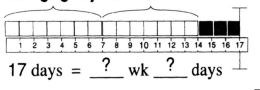

| | | | | | | | | | | | | | | | | |
|1|2|3|4|5|6|7|8|9|10|11|12|13|14|15|16|17|

17 days = $\underline{\ ?\ }$ wk $\underline{\ ?\ }$ days

Think: How many 7s in 17? $7\overline{)17}$ R ___

17 days = $\underline{\quad}$ wk $\underline{\quad}$ days

Days	How many 7s?	Weeks and days
60 days	$7\overline{)60}$ = ___ R ___	60 days = ___ wk ___ days
45 days	$7\overline{)}$ = ___ R ___	45 days = ___ wk ___ days
50 days	$7\overline{)}$ = ___ R ___	50 days = ___ wk ___ day

110

YEARS AND MONTHS

A

Changing years to months

One Year

J	F	M	A	M	J	J	A	S	O	N	D

1 year = 12 months

J	F	M	A	M	J	J	A	S	O	N	D
J	F	M	A	M	J	J	A	S	O	N	D

2 yrs = 24 mos

> 12 is the key number in problems about years (yr) and months (mo).

3 years = __?__ months

3 yr = __3__ × __12__ = __36__ mo

5 yr = __5__ × ____ = ____ mo   3 yr 3 mo = ____ × ____ + ____ = ____ mo

2 yr = ____ × ____ = ____ mo   5 yr 6 mo = ____ × ____ + ____ = ____ mo

---

B

Changing months to years

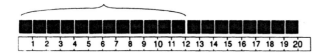

1	2	3	4	5	6	7	8	9	10	11	12	13	14	15	16	17	18	19	20

The baby is 20 months old.

20 months = __?__ years __?__ months

Think: How many 12s in 20? $12\overline{)20}$ R __

The baby is _____ year, _____ months old.

Months	How many 12s?	Years and months
64 months	$12\overline{)64}$ R __	64 mo = _____ yr _____ mo
30 months	$12\overline{)30}$ R __	30 mo = _____ yr _____ mo

I lived in France for 3 years, 6 months. That was _____ months.

A

Fill in the blanks.

1 meter = _____ centimeters   1 dime = _____ cents

1 foot = _____ inches   1 nickel = _____ cents

1 yard = _____ feet   1 dollar = _____ cents

B

1 gallon = _____ quarts   1 year = _____ months

1 quart = _____ cups   1 month = _____ weeks

1 pint = _____ cups   1 week = _____ days

C

Mrs. Torres gets 4 magazines each month. How many magazines does she get in 1 year?

Molly is 54 inches tall. How many feet and inches is that?

She gets _____ magazines a year.

54 inches is _____ feet, _____ inches.

Ana is buying a ribbon for her 3 dolls. If each doll's ribbon is 18 inches long, how long a ribbon must Anna buy?

Henry will be in England for 18 months. How much more than 1 year will that be?

She must buy a ribbon _____ inches long.

That will be _____ months more than a year.

The recipe for rice calls for 2 cups of milk. If we double the recipe, how much milk will we use?

John has art lessons for 2 hours each week. How many hours is that in 1 month?

We will use _____ cups, or _____ quart, of milk.

In 1 month John takes art lessons for _____ hours.

112

Chris earned $48 last month. How much did he earn each week?

He earned $_____ a week.

Mike sleeps 8 hours every night. He figures that must be _____ hours a week!

If Maddy drinks 2 cups of milk every day, how many quarts does she drink in a week?

Jake cleans the garage once a month. At the end of the year he had earned $84. About how much did he earn each month?

Maddy drinks _____ quarts and _____ cups a week.

Jake earned $_____ a month.

Each week Grandmother spends about $28 for food on Monday, $17 on Wednesday, and $38 on Friday. About how much does she spend a month on food?

The teacher wants each child to read 200 pages a week. If Joseph read 27 pages on Monday and 58 pages on Wednesday, how many more pages must he read?

She spends $_____ a month.

Joseph must read _____ more pages.

Chicago is 1,000 miles from Boston. If the Wongs drive 315 miles on Monday and 432 miles on Tuesday, how many more miles must they drive?

The boat costs $500. If Lamar has $119 in the bank and earned $263 cutting grass, how much more money does he need?

The Wongs must drive _____ more miles.

Lamar needs $_____ more.

1 whole

This is 1 whole.

This is 1 whole divided into 2 equal parts.

$\frac{1}{2}$

This is $\frac{1}{2}$ of the equal parts.

Write: $\frac{1}{2}$. Say: one-half.

This is 1 whole divided into 4 equal parts.

$\frac{1}{4}$

This is $\frac{1}{4}$ of the equal parts.

Write: $\frac{1}{4}$. Say: one-fourth.

$\frac{1}{4}$			

Write $\frac{1}{4}$ on each fraction.

Color $\frac{2}{4}$ red.

$\frac{1}{4}$			

Write $\frac{1}{4}$ on each fraction.

Color $\frac{3}{4}$ red.

A

This is 1 whole.

This is $\dfrac{1}{8}$ of the equal parts.

Write: $\dfrac{1}{8}$. Say: one-eighth.

Color the $\dfrac{1}{8}$ black.

B

Write $\dfrac{1}{8}$ on each fraction.

Color $\dfrac{4}{8}$ red. Color $\dfrac{2}{8}$ green.

C

Write $\dfrac{1}{8}$ on each fraction.

Color each $\dfrac{1}{8}$ orange. One whole is $\dfrac{}{8}$.

Write $\dfrac{1}{4}$ on each fraction.

Color each $\dfrac{1}{4}$ blue. One whole is $\dfrac{}{4}$.

ADDING LIKE FRACTIONS

A

1 whole

$\frac{1}{2}$	$\frac{1}{2}$

Color $\frac{1}{2}$ green. Color $\frac{1}{2}$ red.

$$\frac{1}{2} \; + \; \frac{1}{2} \; = \; \frac{}{2} \; = \; \mathbf{1}$$

B

$\frac{1}{4}$	$\frac{1}{4}$	$\frac{1}{4}$	$\frac{1}{4}$

Color $\frac{3}{4}$ blue. Color $\frac{1}{4}$ red.

$$\frac{3}{4} \; + \; \frac{1}{4} \; = \; \frac{}{4} \; = \; \mathbf{1}$$

C

$$\frac{1}{4} \; + \; \frac{1}{4} \; = \; \frac{}{4} \qquad\qquad \frac{1}{2} \; + \; \frac{1}{2} \; = \; \frac{}{2} \; = $$

$$\frac{2}{4} \; + \; \frac{1}{4} \; = \; \frac{}{4} \qquad\qquad \frac{2}{4} \; + \; \frac{2}{4} \; = \; \frac{}{4} \; = $$

$$\frac{3}{4} \; + \; \frac{1}{4} \; = \; \frac{}{4} \; = \qquad\qquad \frac{1}{4} \; + \; \frac{3}{4} \; = \; \frac{}{4} \; = $$

A

1 whole

$\frac{1}{4}$	$\frac{1}{4}$	$\frac{1}{4}$	$\frac{1}{4}$

Color $\frac{2}{4}$ blue. Color $\frac{2}{4}$ red.

$$\frac{2}{4} \quad + \quad \frac{2}{4} \quad = \quad 1$$

B

$\frac{1}{8}$	$\frac{1}{8}$	$\frac{1}{8}$	$\frac{1}{8}$	$\frac{1}{8}$	$\frac{1}{8}$	$\frac{1}{8}$	$\frac{1}{8}$

Color $\frac{6}{8}$ orange. Color $\frac{2}{8}$ red.

$$\frac{6}{8} \quad + \quad \frac{2}{8} \quad = \quad 1$$

C

$$\frac{1}{4} \quad + \quad \frac{2}{4} \quad = \qquad\qquad \frac{2}{4} \quad + \quad \frac{1}{4} \quad =$$

$$\frac{2}{8} \quad + \quad \frac{1}{8} \quad = \qquad\qquad \frac{3}{8} \quad + \quad \frac{3}{8} \quad =$$

$$\frac{3}{8} \quad + \quad \frac{2}{8} \quad = \qquad\qquad \frac{4}{8} \quad + \quad \frac{3}{8} \quad =$$

SUBTRACTING LIKE FRACTIONS

A

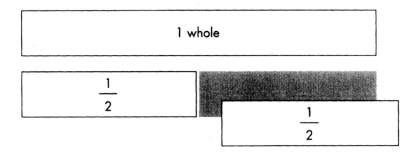

$$\frac{2}{2} \quad - \quad \frac{1}{2} \quad = \quad \frac{}{2}$$

B

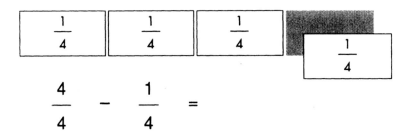

$$\frac{4}{4} \quad - \quad \frac{1}{4} \quad =$$

$$\frac{5}{8} \quad - \quad \frac{2}{8} \quad =$$

C

$$\frac{7}{8} - \frac{2}{8} = \frac{}{8} \qquad \frac{2}{4} - \frac{1}{4} = \qquad \frac{2}{2} - \frac{1}{2} =$$

$$\frac{3}{4} - \frac{2}{4} = \frac{}{4} \qquad \frac{8}{8} - \frac{6}{8} = \qquad \frac{7}{8} - \frac{4}{8} =$$

A This is $\frac{9}{8}$. We call $\frac{9}{8}$ an **improper fraction** because it is greater than one whole.

| $\frac{1}{8}$ | $\frac{1}{8}$ | $\frac{1}{8}$ | $\frac{1}{8}$ | $\frac{1}{8}$ | $\frac{1}{8}$ | $\frac{1}{8}$ | $\frac{1}{8}$ | $\frac{1}{8}$ |

Color $\frac{8}{8}$ black. $\frac{8}{8} = 1$ whole

| 1 whole | $\frac{1}{8}$ |

$\frac{9}{8} = 1\frac{1}{8}$. We call $1\frac{1}{8}$ a **mixed number.**

B

| $\frac{1}{8}$ | $\frac{1}{8}$ | $\frac{1}{8}$ | $\frac{1}{8}$ | $\frac{1}{8}$ | $\frac{1}{8}$ | $\frac{1}{8}$ | $\frac{1}{8}$ | $\frac{1}{8}$ | $\frac{1}{8}$ | $\frac{1}{8}$ |

This is $\frac{11}{8}$. Color $\frac{8}{8}$ black.

$\frac{11}{8} = 1\frac{}{8}$

C

| $\frac{1}{4}$ | $\frac{1}{4}$ | $\frac{1}{4}$ | $\frac{1}{4}$ | $\frac{1}{4}$ |

This is $\frac{5}{4}$. Color $\frac{4}{4}$ black.

| 1 whole | $\frac{1}{4}$ |

$\frac{5}{4} = 1\frac{}{4}$

D Write these improper fractions as mixed numbers.

$\frac{9}{8} =$ \qquad $\frac{5}{4} =$ \qquad $\frac{4}{2} =$ \qquad $\frac{6}{4} =$

A This is $1\frac{3}{8}$. It is a mixed number.

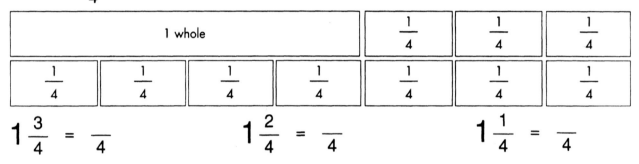

| 1 whole | | $\frac{1}{8}$ | $\frac{1}{8}$ | $\frac{1}{8}$ |

$1\frac{3}{8}$

| $\frac{1}{8}$ | $\frac{1}{8}$ | $\frac{1}{8}$ | $\frac{1}{8}$ | $\frac{1}{8}$ | $\frac{1}{8}$ | $\frac{1}{8}$ | $\frac{1}{8}$ | $\frac{1}{8}$ | $\frac{1}{8}$ | $\frac{1}{8}$ |

$\frac{8}{8} + \frac{3}{8} = \frac{11}{8}$

$1\frac{3}{8} = \frac{}{8}$ $1\frac{5}{8} = \frac{}{8}$ $1\frac{7}{8} = \frac{}{8}$

$1\frac{1}{8} = \frac{}{8}$ $1\frac{2}{8} = \frac{}{8}$ $1\frac{6}{8} = \frac{}{8}$

B This is $1\frac{3}{4}$.

| 1 whole | | | | $\frac{1}{4}$ | $\frac{1}{4}$ | $\frac{1}{4}$ |

| $\frac{1}{4}$ | $\frac{1}{4}$ | $\frac{1}{4}$ | $\frac{1}{4}$ | $\frac{1}{4}$ | $\frac{1}{4}$ | $\frac{1}{4}$ |

$1\frac{3}{4} = \frac{}{4}$ $1\frac{2}{4} = \frac{}{4}$ $1\frac{1}{4} = \frac{}{4}$

C This is $1\frac{1}{2}$.

| 1 whole | | $\frac{1}{2}$ |

| $\frac{1}{2}$ | $\frac{1}{2}$ | $\frac{1}{2}$ |

$1\frac{1}{2} = \frac{}{2}$ $2\frac{1}{2} = \frac{}{2}$

D

Write these mixed numbers as improper fractions.

$1\frac{1}{8} = \frac{}{8}$ $1\frac{1}{4} = \frac{}{4}$ $1\frac{1}{2} = \frac{}{2}$ $1\frac{3}{4} = \frac{}{4}$

A

Add.

$$\frac{1}{4} + \frac{2}{4} =$$ $$\frac{1}{2} + \frac{1}{2} =$$ $$\frac{5}{8} + \frac{2}{8} =$$

$$\frac{4}{8} + \frac{1}{8} =$$ $$\frac{3}{8} + \frac{2}{8} =$$ $$\frac{3}{4} + \frac{1}{4} =$$

B

Subtract.

$$\frac{3}{4} - \frac{2}{4} =$$ $$\frac{2}{2} - \frac{1}{2} =$$ $$\frac{3}{8} - \frac{2}{8} =$$

$$\frac{7}{8} - \frac{5}{8} =$$ $$\frac{5}{8} - \frac{4}{8} =$$ $$\frac{4}{4} - \frac{1}{4} =$$

C

Write as mixed numbers.

$$\frac{5}{4} = 1\frac{}{4}$$ $$\frac{9}{8} =$$ $$\frac{3}{2} =$$

$$\frac{11}{8} =$$ $$\frac{7}{4} =$$ $$\frac{10}{8} =$$

D

Write as improper fractions.

$$1\frac{1}{4} = \frac{}{4}$$ $$1\frac{1}{2} =$$ $$1\frac{3}{4} =$$

$$2\frac{1}{2} = \frac{}{2}$$ $$1\frac{3}{8} =$$ $$1\frac{5}{8} =$$

E

Our dog had **6** puppies. We divided them between **2** children. How many did each get?

The cook baked **8** apple tarts and divided them among **4** children. How many did each child get?

Each child got _____ puppies.

Each child got _____ tarts.

121

A

65	38	53	35	37	524
+ 29	+ 37	− 38	+ 58	− 19	− 458

13	56	76	55	62	287
+ 49	− 48	− 27	+ 37	− 27	+ 696

B

Write the number three hundred forty-six. _____

Write the number five hundred seven. _____

Write the number seven hundred sixty. _____

Write the number one hundred three. _____

C

13	28	15	16	39	31
25	16	47	21	23	34
+ 34	+ 35	+ 36	+ 38	+ 28	+ 28

D

Abe is reading a book that is **267** pages long. He is on page **189**. How many more pages does he have to read?

Ms. Bass drove **234** miles on Monday. She drove **178** miles on Tuesday. How many miles did she drive in all?

He has to read _____ more pages.

Ms. Bass drove _____ miles.

A

What time is it?

1. What time is it on the second clock in the first row? _____ 4 o'clock _____

2. What time is it on the first clock in the second row? _____

3. What time is it on the first clock in the first row? _____

4. What time is it on the second clock in the second row? _____

B

If you start at 4:30 and read for 20 minutes, at what time will you stop?

If you go out at 5:10 and play for half an hour, when must you stop?

You will stop at _____.

You must stop at _____.

C

Add or subtract.

$ 2.26	$ 7.80	$ 6.30	$ 8.08	$ 5.50
+ 1.45	+ .62	− 1.75	− .39	+ 2.75
$.	$.	$.	$.	$.

D

   Nicole's mother gave her $5.00 and sent her to the store. She has to buy crackers, which cost $1.59, oatmeal, which costs $1.69, and a fig cake for $1.55. How much change should Nicole get from the $5.00?

   Dad bought some presents for Valentine's Day. A bunch of roses for Mother cost $4.29, valentines for the children cost $1.99, and handkerchiefs for Grandmother cost $2.25. He gave the clerk ten dollars. How much change did he get back?

Nicole should get $____.____back.

Dad got back $____.____.

A

8 × 6	7 × 7	4 × 8	7 × 4	6 × 9	7 × 5	3 × 7
6 × 6	8 × 3	7 × 8	6 × 7	6 × 4	9 × 8	6 × 8
5 × 7	9 × 6	7 × 6	5 × 8	9 × 5	4 × 7	8 × 8

B

23 × 6	32 × 7	45 × 8	54 × 9	66 × 5	87 × 4
65 × 8	57 × 9	88 × 7	74 × 6	38 × 4	85 × 3

C

Daryl is 18 years old. His grandfather is 4 times as old as he is. How old is his grandfather?

Stephanie makes $95 each week by delivering newspapers. How much will she make in 4 weeks?

His grandfather is _____ years old.

Stephanie will make $_____.

124

A

$4\overline{)24}$ $7\overline{)56}$ $6\overline{)36}$ $9\overline{)63}$ $4\overline{)32}$ $7\overline{)63}$ $8\overline{)56}$

$8\overline{)40}$ $9\overline{)45}$ $7\overline{)35}$ $8\overline{)64}$ $6\overline{)54}$ $9\overline{)36}$ $7\overline{)49}$

$7\overline{)42}$ $8\overline{)72}$ $6\overline{)48}$ $9\overline{)54}$ $8\overline{)48}$ $9\overline{)72}$ $6\overline{)42}$

B

$20 \div 5 = \underline{\hspace{1cm}}$ $81 \div 9 = \underline{\hspace{1cm}}$ $36 \div 4 = \underline{\hspace{1cm}}$ $30 \div 6 = \underline{\hspace{1cm}}$

C

$40\overline{)160}$ $20\overline{)180}$ $30\overline{)210}$ $50\overline{)250}$ $60\overline{)420}$

$5\overline{)33}$ R __ $9\overline{)46}$ R __ $6\overline{)29}$ R __ $5\overline{)21}$ R __ $8\overline{)60}$ R __

$7\overline{)32}$ R __ $5\overline{)39}$ R __ $8\overline{)35}$ R __ $5\overline{)44}$ R __ $9\overline{)80}$ R __

D

The teacher asked the children to arrange **27** paintings in rows of **6**. How many rows can the children make? How many paintings will be left over?

The children can make _____ rows of **6** paintings. _____ paintings will be left over.

There are **36** children on the playground. If they form **4** equal teams, how many children will be on each team?

There will be _____ children on each team.

A

Olga is selling birthday cards. She sold 8 cards to Mrs. Jackson and 16 cards to Mr. Thompson. She began with 36 cards. How many cards does she have left?

Olga has _____ cards left.

The scout troop is making scarves from a strip of cloth 15 feet long. If each scarf is 3 feet long, how many scarves can the scouts make?

They can make _____ scarves.

On Monday Makoto read 35 pages of his new book. On Tuesday he read 22 pages and today, 29 pages. His book is 200 pages long. How many pages are left for Makoto to read?

Makoto has _____ pages left to read.

After school Ellen spends 30 minutes doing her homework. Her sister spends twice as long doing her homework. How long does Ellen's sister work?

Ellen's sister works _____ minutes, or _____ hour.

Mr. Prince just bought 8 new dresses for his dress shop. If each dress cost $60, how much did he spend?

Mr. Prince spent $_____.

The gas tank in my car holds 12 gallons. If I just put in 6 gallons to fill it up, how many gallons were already in it?

There were already _____ gallons in it.

B Complete these charts.

year	1	2	3	5
months	12			

weeks	1	2	3	
days	7			28

yards	1	2	10		20
feet	3			36	

feet	1	2	3	5
inches				

Column 1	Column 2	Column 3	Column 4
$\frac{1}{8}$	$\frac{1}{4}$	$\frac{1}{2}$	1 Whole
$\frac{1}{8}$			
$\frac{1}{8}$	$\frac{1}{4}$		
$\frac{1}{8}$			
$\frac{1}{8}$	$\frac{1}{4}$	$\frac{1}{2}$	
$\frac{1}{8}$			
$\frac{1}{8}$	$\frac{1}{4}$		
$\frac{1}{8}$			

Made in the USA